FISH COP

OTHER BOOKS BY ROBERT J. ADAMS

*   *   *

THE STUMP FARM

BEYOND THE STUMP FARM

HORSE COP

THE ELEPHANT'S TRUNK

THE SOUTH ROAD

FISH COP

ROBERT J. ADAMS

MEGAMY

Copyright © by Robert J. Adams and Kelly Hymanyk
First Printed in 1999
2ⁿᵈ Printing 2001
Printed in Canada

THE PUBLISHER:
Megamy Publishing Ltd.
P. O. Box 3507
Spruce Grove, Alberta, Canada T7X 3A7
E-Mail megamy@compusmart.ab.ca

Canadian Cataloguing in Publication Data
Adams, Robert J., 1938-
    Fish Cop

ISBN 0-9681916-4-9

    1. Adams, Robert J., 1938- --Anecdotes.   2. Game
wardens--Alberta–Anecdotes. 3. Alberta. Fish and Wildlife
Division–Anecdotes. 4. Canadian wit and humor (English).
I. Title.

HV7911.A32A3 1999   C818'.5402   C99-900213-9

Senior Editor: Kelly Hymanyk
Copy Editor: R. John Hayes
Design, Layout and Production: Kelly Hymanyk
Cover: Rage Studios Inc.
Printing: Jasper Printing

DEDICATION

To my daughter Kelly, she is my inspiration for writing. Without her, none of this would have been possible.

CONTENTS

DISCLAIMER

The stories you are about to read are all true. The men, women and children you will read about are all people from my past. I have taken the liberty of changing the names of many of them to protect their identities. Although I view the past as being very humorous, they may not.

ACKNOWLEDGEMENTS

To my family, Martha, Kelly, Bill, Megan and Amy, who have all given so much of their time and effort. It was with their understanding and patience that I was able to complete this manuscript.

To the staff of the Fish & Wildlife Division, with whom I worked during my early years as an officer. Special thanks to Charlie Scott, who was a walking encyclopedia on fisheries in Alberta and Jerry Pelchat who taught me all about pheasants and transects. All provided a solid base for the learning experience that continued for 33 years.

To the Ducks Unlimited crew in Brooks for the memorable experiences. Special thanks to George (Mr. Ducks Unlimited) Freeman.

INTRODUCTION

Laugh until you cry as Adams' vibrant humor continues to explode in "FISH COP." What better vehicle for laughter than to recount days gone by.

Once again Adams finds humor in real life situations. Situations that might defeat a lesser man. But not Adams, his unique perspective turns ordinary, bizarre, frustrating and even mundane occurrences into witty stories that are a must read for young and old alike.

Thank you Mr. Adams for continuing to tickle the funny bone and for providing an avenue to laugh out loud.

MEGAMY PUBLISHING

FISH COP

FISH COP

"Good luck, hon," Mar called and waved from the little red Volkswagen Beetle.

"Good luck, Bobby," Mom added.

Proud words of encouragement echoed through the parking lot as I strode away. I was so excited, so filled with anticipation that I decided to forego the law and the safety of the cross-walk. I didn't take the time to walk to the corner and cross at the lights; instead, I raced across 9th Avenue, jaywalking, dodging the traffic.

When I reached the safety of the sidewalk, I paused briefly on the cement stairs at the front of the old gray sandstone building, and gazed up at the huge oak doors. Then, I charged forward. I took the steps two, three at a time as I raced toward my destiny. I was so excited. I could hardly contain myself.

It was October 20, 1960, 8:30 a.m., when I walked into the Natural Resources Building, in Edmonton. Here, in this rustic old building, I would be sworn in as the newest fish and wildlife officer in the Province of Alberta. It was an exciting time and my heart was racing.

Inside the old building, in the cramped space that was allotted to the Fish & Wildlife Division, I met the Powers-that-be. The brains of the organization. The hub around which the fish and wildlife business flowed in widening, never-ending circles until it reached the far corners of the province. I met each and every one of them. Each was some kind of boss and all of them would be senior to me. Once again, I was the bottom rung, the lowest man on the totem pole. But it mattered not, for I was going to be a game warden. A fish cop. I was on a high. It was a dream come true and I was on the top of the world.

Once inside, I introduced myself to a friendly gal who escorted me into the office of the director, the top man. This was the man who reported directly to the deputy minister.

"This is the man you want to talk to," she said smiling. "He runs the whole show."

After a few pleasantries, the director took me in and introduced me to the administrator, the second in charge.

"This is the man who really runs the show," he chuckled. "He has a finger on the pulse of the division. If you ever need anything or have any questions, you just call him. He'll look after you."

It was the administrator who showed me around and introduced me to the rest of the headquarters group. I met the chief clerk.

"This is the man who keeps the show running," he informed me. The chief clerk was so busy, he hardly had time to say hello before others descended upon him. "I can't tell you how much that man means to this division," said the administrator, and he shook his head. "Without him, the show would grind to a halt." We both watched as the chief clerk dipped and dodged between boxes and desks, then hustled away to deal with the latest crisis.

I was introduced to a number of biologists. Their offices held a vast collection of jars, full of pickled fish, assorted embryos, and a variety of animal parts and pieces.

"These guys don't have districts; they work throughout the province," I was advised. It was obvious that each ran his own show.

"Now these lovely ladies," said the administrator. "They're the real brains of the outfit and they really are the ones who keep the whole show running. Adams, my friend, a word to the wise: you stay on the good side of the secretaries. If you want to know what's happening, all you have to do is ask the secretaries. They know and, if they like you, you'll know too."

Last, but not least, in the far reaches of the cramped quarters, we found them. Tucked away, out of sight, were the fish and wildlife officers: real live bodies, two of them. I didn't need an introduction. I could tell who they were by their uniforms. I felt sure that they, too, must have run some part of the show. There was no explanation of the officers' role, or which part of the show they ran. I figured, it was probably just an oversight.

My head was swimming by the time I had made the rounds. In a few short minutes, I had been introduced to the headquarters crew. I had met them all, they who were the Powers-that-be.

We were still walking around the office, picking our way between the boxes and desks.

"Well, Adams, we better get you sworn at and get you on your way," said the administrator. He stopped at a desk, where one of the real brains of the outfit was sitting, one of the people who really kept the whole thing running. It was one of the secretaries. I would come to realize, as the years rolled by, that he was right, it was the secretaries who were the real backbone of the Fish & Wildlife Division. They were the ones who kept everything moving.

"Bob, could I get your autograph on these?" she asked.

"Sure thing," I replied.

"Sign here," she said, pointing to a spot on the bottom of a sheet of paper. "And here." She pointed to a second sheet. "And here." She pointed to a third sheet. "This one is the most important," she chuckled. I carefully eyeballed the most important document requiring my signature. It was the income tax form. "Do you want income tax to be deducted as a married or single person?" she asked. "This is just for income tax purposes, of course," she assured me.

"Single," I replied.

"Oh," she giggled "You're not married then?"

"Only for income tax purposes," I responded.

"Oh," she sort of mumbled. Then she gathered up the papers. "Okay, that's all," she replied and went back to keeping the whole show running.

"Well, how does it feel?" asked the number two man.

"How does what feel?" I asked.

"How does it feel to be a game warden, to be sworn in?"

"I don't know," I replied, somewhat at a loss for words. "Was I sworn in?"

"You signed the oaths, didn't you?"

"Yeah, I guess, but...."

"Good. Good, and now that you're sworn in," chuckled the number two man as he fumbled through a desk drawer, "you'll be needing one of these."

"Thanks," I replied as I took the little square blue box from him. I was busy admiring the little box when he interrupted.

"Go ahead. Look at it, Mr. Adams," he urged with a big smile on his face. "Open it up."

I lifted the lid and there, on the inside, lying on a bed of white cotton, was a badge. It was a circle of silver with the bronze head of a big horn sheep. The head was raised and riveted to the silver. It was a conservation officer's badge. My badge. I quickly noted the number: # 63. There had not been very many fish and wildlife officers ahead of me in this division, I thought.

"Thanks," I replied, then put the lid on the box and

stuffed it into my pants pocket.

"Are you driving to Brooks today?"

"I thought I'd go as far as Strathmore today and onto Brooks tomorrow ... if that's all right?" I added.

"That's fine," he assured me. "You'll be needing some equipment. Come with me and we'll see what we can rustle up. Since you're driving, you might as well take it with you."

"I'm going to be taking my equipment with me?" I asked. This was not good news. Where am I going to put it, I wondered? The beetle was already packed. Every available inch of space had something crammed into it. In fact, almost everything Mar and I owned was in the beetle. And the load also included Mom. Mar and Mom were sharing the passenger's seat and the emergency brake located between the two front seats. I had no room for equipment. However, I reluctantly followed the number two man to receive my kit. This was not good.

Somewhere in the back of the complex, in front of an old bookcase, we stopped. From one shelf, he selected a copy of the Alberta Game Act and an assortment of regulations. From another shelf, he found a copy of the Fisheries Act of Canada, with more regulations.

I had a handful of legislation when he asked, "What kinda rifle do you shoot, Adams?"

"Oh, I've shot a 303, a 30-06 and a 45-70," I replied.

"Okay, here you are," he said, and handed me a box of shells. I looked at the box. They were for a 303.

"What are these for?" I asked rather foolishly.

"They're for you," he replied. "Each man gets a box of shells issued to him."

"Thanks," I replied, and waited for the rifle.

Then he got down on his hands and knees and almost disappeared into the bottom shelf. He rustled through several boxes before he finally pulled out a well-worn leather case. "You'll be needing these as well," he mumbled.

"What's that," I asked, and quickly noted that the case was far too small for a rifle.

"Binoculars," he replied. "You want a pair of binoculars, don't you?"

"Right," I answered as I took the case. Actually, I wanted some of everything I could get. "I can always use a good pair of binoculars." I looked the case over carefully, but it was not very promising. I could only hope that the binoculars hidden inside were in better shape than the case.

"Well, let me see now … that looks to be about it my friend," he said after he had thoroughly checked each shelf.

"That's it? That's all?" I asked. "What about the gun, the rifle that goes with these shells?"

"Use your own," he replied. "You said you shot a 303, didn't you?"

"Well, yeah, I've shot one, but …."

"Well then, use it," he said emphatically. "We'll give you a box of shells a year."

"I gotta use my own gun," I replied, and sort of chuckled in disbelief. "But …." I started to say I don't have one, then I quickly changed my mind. Not having

19

a gun could be the difference in getting this job or not.

"What about a uniform?" I asked. "Don't I get a uniform?"

"When you leave here, you can stop by LaFleche Brothers. They'll measure you up."

"Do I wait for the uniform?" I asked.

"We'll ship it to you when it's ready," he assured me. "In the meantime, just wear your own clothes."

"And, uh, what about training?" I inquired. "Is there any training for new recruits?"

"Didn't you just get out of the mounted police?" he asked.

"Yeah, sure. I had 10 months of training there, but they didn't teach us nothing about being a game warden."

"I think you've had enough training," he replied.

I was almost afraid to ask the next question. "What about a vehicle?" I asked. "Do I get to drive my own car?"

"No. No. Don't worry about a vehicle. We've already looked after you, young fella. There's a perfectly good station wagon waiting for you at Brooks," he replied.

"You mean, I can't drive my own car?"

"No," he replied firmly. "You use the station wagon."

"Sure, thanks," I mumbled again. I had been hoping that I could have gone on private mileage to help with the payments on the beetle. Obviously, that was not to be. I could only hope that the station wagon was in better shape then the binocular case.

I put my shoulder to the huge oak doors and pushed my way through, out into the sunlight. Slowly, I walked down the steps that, a short time ago, I felt like I had flown over. In one hand, I carried my equipment. Anybody, even I, would be able to find room in the beetle for a few pieces of paper, a box of shells, a beat-up binocular case and, of course, the blue box with the badge in it.

I walked to the corner, to the traffic lights, waited for the lights to turn green, then safely crossed the road. I returned to the red Volkswagen beetle and my cheering section.

"How'd it go?" Mar asked enthusiastically when I arrived at the car.

"Okay," I replied.

"Did you get sworn in?" It was an important question.

"I ... yeah, I ... I think so," I replied.

"What do you mean, you think so? Don't you know?"

"Well," I replied. "I got a badge."

BADGES AND SARDINES

I can honestly say that, on my first visit to Brooks, the town was everything that I had expected: a small prairie town set out in the middle of the Alberta prairie. There were miles and miles of nothing but never-ending grassland surrounding the immediate area. That was an oasis of rich farm land and shelter belts of trees, thanks to the irrigation system that fed it. But, outside the reach of the irrigation system, there was prairie. Flat, never-ending prairie. Short grass prairie, made even shorter by the many head of cattle that grazed it. Had I not spent a good portion of the past year in Saskatchewan, I would have been in for one big surprise.

No, I was not disappointed in Brooks or the surrounding countryside. And, right on the main drag, I found the Fish & Wildlife Office.

"Look," I said to Mar, "it's right beside the bank. Whenever I need a little cash, I'll be able to pop in and stock up." We both laughed, for at that point, we had neither a bank account nor enough money to open one. But money was the furthest thing from my mind. It was time to meet my new boss and inspect my new digs.

The office, I quickly found out, was at the top of a steep flight of stairs, on the second floor. Once again I bounded up stairs, taking the steps two, three at a time. I wasn't sure if I had been sworn in, but I had a badge and this had to be where I belonged.

I strutted through the door with all the confidence in the world, just like I owned the place. Inside, there were three doors. All open. I looked into each. Two offices contained desks, empty desks, one far emptier then the other. One door led to an empty room out back. I turned to the counter and looked at the desk beyond. There, behind the desk, sitting at a typewriter, sat a lady. The secretary. She was watching me with what I assumed was an annoyed curious look.

"Can I help you?" asked the secretary.

"You bet," I chuckled. "I'm Adams."

That little revelation was greeted with a blank stare. Obviously the name meant nothing to her. "That's nice," she replied. Then asked again. "Can I help you?"

"I'm Bob Adams," I repeated. I still got the blank stare. "I'm your new officer here."

"Here," she repeated and the blank stare was replaced with a look that showed more than just a little surprise. She looked down at the typewriter, then around the desk and the room, searching for something that didn't appear to be there, before looking at me again.

"You? You're the new officer here?" she asked like it was the most incredible thing she had heard.

"Yeah," I replied uneasily. "Me. You were expecting me?" I asked. I was beginning to feel a little foolish and a whole lot deflated by this unexpected turn of events.

"No."

"You didn't know I was coming?"

"No."

"That's okay," I chuckled. "The boss man knows I'm coming. Where would I find him?"

"He's out on patrol," she replied. "It's hunting season, you know?"

"Fine," I smiled, hoping to set her at ease. "I'll just wait for him then."

"Suit yourself," she replied, returning to her typewriter. She paused, then added, "I hope you brought a sleeping bag, because I'm not expecting him back for a few days."

"You're kidding me," I replied. The look convinced me; she wasn't kidding. "Well, I understand there's supposed to be a station wagon ... here ... for me," I sort of mumbled. "You ... you wouldn't happen to know where that might be?"

"No, I wouldn't," she replied.

"They told me in Edmonton that there was a new station wagon here for me."

"They?" she asked. "Who's they?"

"The Powers-that-be," I said and waved my hand in a northerly direction.

This was, to say the least, a very humiliating experience. I wasn't sure what kind of reception I had expected, but I knew that this wasn't it. For a few seconds, I don't know who was more uncomfortable, me or the poor lady behind the counter. I watched as she calmly picked up the phone and dialed a number. I knew then that it was me, I was the more uncomfortable of the two. Had she seen a number of nut-cases over the years? Was I just another one of them? There was some guarded conversation before she hung up the receiver.

"I guess you are coming here, after all," she said, looking surprised. "You can find your station wagon parked in a yard back towards the highway," she advised me before returning to the typewriter.

"Back towards the highway?" I asked.

"You'll be able to see it from the road," she replied without looking up.

Armed with these directions, I shuffled out of the office to look for my new vehicle. From the road, I spotted a station wagon. It was sitting like a horrible green gob between two huge white houses. I drove on by and I prayed it was not mine, but my prayers were to no avail for there were no more station wagons along that stretch of road. In fact, there were no more houses. I returned and parked my almost brand new red Volkswagen Beetle a long way from the green station wagon. Strange things have been known to happen to new vehicles parked along side of old heaps. And a heap it was. The doors were locked and I tried to get a peek at the inside. No dice. I could barely see daylight through the streaky, dust-caked windows, let alone what was inside.

"Lookit the skins," I grumbled to Mar. Except for the protruding wires, the tires had about as much tread on them as a blown up balloon.

"Well, what do you think?" I mumbled to Mar.

"I'm certainly glad I don't have to drive it," she replied.

"It'll be fine," I replied unconvincingly. "It probably just needs to be washed up." But I had to agree that from the outside it looked real bad.

I knocked on the door of the white house that had curtains in it and was greeted by a very friendly lady. The station wagon was parked in the district officer's yard and I was talking to his wife. She gave me the keys to the station wagon, some instructions and some welcome information. I was to stay in the office and familiarize myself with the acts and regulations until the return of the boss man.

A blast of hot stale air hit me when I opened the driver's door of the green station wagon.

"What stinks?" Mar gasped and backed away from the open door.

I hastened around to the passenger's door and opened it to let some fresh air enter. Mar was right, something stank all right. Something that had been ground into the rugs, I assumed, like fish slime and blood. After all, this filthy green station wagon was a working vehicle.

Finally, I got past the smell and poked my head inside and looked around. It didn't get any better. The inside of the station wagon resembled a garbage dump. There were bottles, cans, bags and papers strewn throughout. Nowhere could the floor covering be seen through the mess. Sadly, I realized that the outside of the green station wagon was in far better shape then the inside.

I felt like a whipped pup and I heaved a heavy sigh of resignation as I brushed aside the cobwebs. I kicked an empty pop bottle and a heap of old papers away from the gas pedal before I reluctantly slid through the dust and settled in behind the steering wheel. I inserted the key and turned it in the ignition. RRRRG growled the engine. RG. RRRG. I pumped the gas pedal furiously and turned the key again. There was a click, then ... nothing. My government vehicle, the green station wagon, was dead.

Back to the white house I strode and again knocked at the door. "The station wagon's dead," I announced.

"I'm not surprised. Maybe it's because it's been sitting for so long," she replied. "You'll probably need a boost."

"Right," I replied. "I'll probably need a boost." The three of us stood and looked at each other, helplessly.

"What are you going to do?" Mar asked.

"Looks like I'll have to go and see if I can get someone to boost me," I mumbled.

"Have you found a place to live yet?" asked the lady of the house as we were preparing to leave to search for a boost.

"No," I replied.

"I think the house next door is for rent," she said.

"You might want to check it out. I think you'll find that it's the only house in town for rent," she added.

She was right. The house next door was the only house in town for rent. The folks who owned it came over to show us the house and boost the green station wagon.

First on the agenda was to get the green station wagon running. After several grudging growling attempts, the motor finally turned over. It sat in the yard, sputtering and spitting, while we checked the house out.

"Fifty dollars a month and we pay the utilities," stated the owner.

"Fifty bucks," I whistled. "Man that's a lot of money for an old house."

"It's a pretty good deal, young fella," replied the landlord.

"I don't know about that," I said. "It seems to be a little cool in here. And look at the windows and at the cracks. Man, they're big enough to drive a truck through." I walked over to the windows and put my hand by the window sill.

"Here," I said. "Put your hand here. Feel the draft?"

"I don't feel nothing," he replied.

"Here, right here, feel this," I said. "There's hardly a breeze blowing outside, and inside we've got a gale blowing through. We'll freeze to death in the winter."

"You won't be cold in this house," he stated. "There's a brand new heating system in it. I converted the old coal burner to natural gas. If you're cold, just turn up the gas."

Well, 50 dollars was all the money I had to my name, so it was time for some fancy footwork. I figured I was a pretty shrewd fellow and was not about to take the first deal offered. I bargained and I wheeled and I dealed. Finally, we agreed on a price and I was very pleased with the deal I negotiated. I got the house for 35 dollars a month and I paid the utilities. With the 15 dollar savings, I now had enough money to last until the end of the month, payday.

"The utilities won't be due until the end of the month and, after all, how much could a few utilities cost?" I chuckled as Mar and I stood by the breezy window and surveyed our first home.

"I think I'll have to stuff some rags in those cracks," Mar said.

"I guess I should have taken Mom up on her offer to lend me some money till the first paycheck came in," I said to Mar. But we were young and independent and we were going to make our own way.

Our new landlord drove out of the yard in his pick-up truck. Mar left next driving our almost new Volkswagen beetle. I brought up the rear in the green station wagon. That filthy thing coughed and sputtered, jerked and jumped, begrudging every turn of the tires as I left the yard and nursed it onto the roadway. I cursed every bolt in her.

For the next few days, until the end of the month, I was destined to sit at my very own desk and read the Wildlife Act, the Fisheries Act and all the regulations that I had been given. I would read them and read them, then I would read them some more. Before the first hour of reading had passed, I began to long for a field trip and some action.

"You should go for coffee and meet some of the fellows," the secretary advised me. It was around 9:30 on my first day.

"Well, that sounds great, but who would I be meeting?" I asked. "I don't know a soul here."

"The Mounties," she replied. "Two or three of them go the Country Kitchen for coffee every morning about this time."

"Thanks," I said. I reached into the pockets of my jeans and pulled out some coins. Just over a dollar. It was all the money I had for coffee and lunches, and the end of the month was still days away. Oh, well, a dollar should be more than enough for a 10 cent coffee, I thought. I grabbed my Edson Athletics baseball jacket, the closest thing I had to a uniform, and walked out the door.

She was right. There were two Mounties sitting at a table having coffee. I walked over to their table. They both looked me up and down, suspiciously, when I introduced myself. I was probably the first fish cop they had seen dressed in a baseball jacket, a white T shirt, jeans and sneakers. I'm gonna have to remember to take my badge with me until I get my uniform, I said to myself, and made a mental note not to leave the office badgeless again.

I was enjoying myself, having coffee, telling old war stories, talking to guys I could identify with. It got even better when another three Mounties and the local magistrate joined us. It was like old home week. Then a part time justice of the peace and another fellow joined us. That was even better. I was meeting all the people I was going to have to work with.

Then came the moment of truth: hands with coins in them appeared on the table. "You know how to play 'birds in the bush'?" someone asked me.

"No," I answered, when I realized that this wasn't "Dutch Treat." As the coins rattled, the hands were tucked under the table. For me, the fun started to leave the happy gathering.

"Take three coins," he replied. "Keep anywhere from none to three in one hand and hold it on the table. We all guess how many coins are in the hands. If you guess, you're out. Last one up pays the bill. Think you can handle that?"

"Barely," I managed to squeak the answer out. Everyone laughed. Everyone but me. Everyone probably had a whole lot more money in their pocket then I did.

Sticking someone, anyone but yourself, was a gala affair. Every loud whoop, and a chorus of curses by the rest, signaled someone, some lucky participant, had guessed the number and dodged a bullet. One by one, the happy players dropped by the way. As the number of hands on the table grew smaller, my hand grew sweatier. In fact, it was so wet and greasy, I thought for sure I was going to drop my coins each time I moved some from one hand to the other. I really was not enjoying myself. Finally, I breathed a sigh of relief when, through no fault of my own, I hit upon the right

31

combination. I knew right then that I had to do something different for coffee breaks. Neither my nerves nor my pocket book could take this pressure twice a day. Until my paycheque arrived, I could not afford to lose a game of "Birds in the Bush." I would stay in the office during coffee breaks and study the Acts and regulations.

"I've got some mail for you," the secretary called to me, about the third day that I had been hiding in my office.

"Mail," I repeated happily. "Mail addressed to me." I raced into the front office and retrieved a neatly wrapped little parcel. There it was, right on the top of the parcel:

> Robert J. Adams,
> Asst. Conservation Officer,
> Brooks, Alberta.

That made it official. Obviously, I had been sworn in and was a bona fide officer after all. Quickly I tore open the wrapping. Inside was a little blue box and inside that, resting on a bed of cotton batting was a badge. #64. Oh yes, I was an officer all right, a penniless, two badge officer.

Then came the day I had been waiting for: payday, the end of the month. Once more I bounded up the steps and charged into the office. Today, I could go for coffee with the boys without worrying if I didn't guess how many birds in the bush there were. Tonight, there would be a steak on the table, with a baked potato and salad.

"Here's your mail, Bob," said the secretary. "But I don't think this is what you've been waiting for," she smiled and handed me a little parcel.

"This doesn't look like my paycheck," I said unhappily. "Unless one of the Powers-that-be took the time to gift wrap it."

"I would say you're right on the first count," she replied. "And you're dead wrong on the second."

"Please, let this be a sick little joke," I moaned as once more I tore off the outer wrapping. She was right. There in front of me was another little blue box. On the inside, another badge: #65. Now I was a chequeless, penniless, three badge officer. There would be no joy in the Adams household tonight. Once more there would be macaroni on the table for supper.

It did not take me long to get on the phone to the Powers-that-be.

"I didn't get my paycheque," I whined and moaned. "I'm broke. I don't even have enough money for a cuppa coffee."

"What, you didn't get your cheque? Just a minute, I'm sure there must be some mistake," came the surprised response. I could hear some muffled discussion in the background. Then: "Mr. Adams, I'm afraid there's been an oversight. It's all my fault. I take full responsibility, and I do apologize, my friend. I guess in the excitement of having you sworn in, we forgot to tell you: you have to be on staff for a month before your first cheque gets processed," came the apologetic reply.

"A month," I moaned. "What am I supposed to do

33

for the next month?" I asked. "I'm flat broke."

"Let me give you a little advice, son," came the soothing words. "When you signed on here, you got a good-paying, full-time government job. You'll get your money. The first cheque just takes a little time. Now, if I was in your boots, I'd be hustling my butt down to the local bank. Talk to the manager, tell him your story. Ask for a small loan, just until your first cheque comes in. I'm sure he'll help you out. I've always found bank managers in small towns to be very understanding."

With heavy heart, I waited for the bank next door to open. Then, with hat in hand and my tail tucked between my legs, I crept in and introduced myself. I explained my predicament and I assured him that I had the best job in town. A permanent, full-time government job. A guaranteed paycheque every month. I pleaded, I whined and finally I groveled. The Powers-that-be were right: small town bank managers were very understanding. In fact, this manager was so understanding he sympathized with me all the way to the door.

"Mr. Adams, you come back and see us when your first cheque arrives," he said sympathetically. "Then I'll be glad to help you." Macaroni was still on the plate for supper.

As I walked into the street, I ran smack dab into a couple of the Mounties. "Hey, Bob," one greeted me. "We've missed you at coffee, old man."

"Sorry guys, I've been pretty busy, you know, with hunting season and all."

"Yeah, we understand," he assured me. "C'mon and

join us, we're just going now and we need some new money in the game."

"Okay. I just have to go up to the office first. I'll see you over there," I lied. I walked through the door and watched until they had entered the restaurant then I jumped in the green station wagon and got lost. That night I made a phone call. Not to a banker, but to another small town lender that I knew. Without having to explain my situation, whine or grovel, I got 50 bucks. It was like I had just won the Irish Sweepstakes. There was easily enough to last me a month. "Thanks, Mom," was all the collateral I needed.

Then came more real-life drama. The Brooks Fish & Wildlife District was one huge piece of real estate. I was destined to spend at least two weeks in the far reaches of the district, in such towns as Empress, Cereal and Oyen. There were hotel rooms to pay for and meals to buy. Suddenly fifty bucks did not appear to be such a windfall after all.

There would be no eating out when I was on the road, on a field trip. I would be brown bagging it.

"Good afternoon, you little devils," I greeted my lunch on my first day on the prairie, secure in the fact that I would not be seen. I realized that the green station wagon would stick out like a sore thumb on the bald ass prairie. I also expected that a stopped vehicle would attract attention, so I went to great lengths to hide. I had picked a nice little gully where I was least likely to be found. In that hole, with a nice breeze whistling through the grass and pushing a few lazy clouds across a deep blue sky, I enjoyed my first lunch on my first field trip. A can of sardines and a couple of slices of bread. When the sardine tin was empty, I used a slice of bread to mop up every last drop of oil.

I flipped the empty can out onto the prairie and sat back. The can picked up the glare of the sun and shot a beam of light back at me. I looked at the empty can lying in the grass, but I didn't see a can. Instead, I saw the image of a cow walking across the prairie with her hoof stuffed into a sardine can. She was wearing it like a shoe. I retrieved the can and flipped it into the back seat. There the odor of old sardines could mix with the rest of the stink in the old green station wagon.

Yes, I could only thank my lucky stars that the IGA store had had sardines on sale. For 10 cents a tin I was able to pick up enough sardines to last for a month of lunches and suppers on the prairies.

Sitting in those little gullies, I had plenty of time to think and take stock of my issue equipment. The first day out, I pulled my new pair of binoculars from their worn out case. I was not really surprised to find that the binoculars matched the case perfectly. Both were old and well worn – both looked like they belonged in a display cabinet in some museum. But the real surprise was yet to come. Raising the glasses to my eyes and peering through the lenses, I saw an amazing sight. The surrounding prairie was not flat with short grass, it was all fuzzy and blurry. Now, I knew that the division would not send a man out into the field with faulty equipment, the binoculars probably just needed a little adjustment. So, I fiddled with them, I turned every dial on them suckers, then I tried to turn parts that didn't or wouldn't turn. First one way, then the other. I tried closing one eye to focus one lense, I tried closing one eye to focus both lenses, but nothing worked. Getting this pair of beaters was probably just an oversight. In the haste to get me equipped, the binoculars had probably been picked up out of the reject pile instead of the issue pile. That was no problem – I'd talk to the Powers-that-be and get a new pair.

For the next month, the pile of sardine cans mounted in the back of the green station wagon. The smell would have choked me if my scent glands had not been destroyed by the collection of stinks and odors already frequenting the interior of the green station wagon. In the meantime, I continued dodging Mounties looking for new money in a game of "birds in the bush" by hiding away in a prairie gully, fiddling with my binoculars and building my collection of empty sardine cans. Then, finally, pay day arrived once more.

I was at the office bright and early, waiting for my cheque. It had been a long wait and I deserved it. In fact, I chuckled to myself, I think I deserved two of them. I stood at the counter and watched eagerly as the secretary sorted the mail and handed out the envelopes. Everyone got an envelope. I eagerly grabbed mine, but it was only the gas bill. Sadly, I realized that another payday had come and gone and still my cheque was conspicuous by its absence. I wasted no time in calling headquarters.

"I didn't get a cheque again this month," I wailed to the Powers-that-be. "What are you people trying to do to me?"

"Slow down, son. Slow down," came the calming voice. "Don't get your shirt in a knot. Let me check it out and see what happened."

"There's more then my shirt in a knot," I mumbled to myself as the phone went silent. While I waited, I opened the gas bill and almost fell through the floor. "Ninety dollars, there must be a mistake," I choked out when I read the amount.

"Adams, are you still there? Did you just say something?" came the voice from a distance.

"Yeah, I'm still here," I replied weakly as I stared at the gas bill.

"Listen lad, didn't I explain to you that it takes a month to process your first cheque?" he asked.

"That was a month ago," I howled, wondering how I was ever going to pay for the gas. "You told me last month, I'd get a cheque this month. I'm two months behind now and I've got a 90 dollar gas bill to boot."

"No. No. No. Lad," he chuckled. "Let me explain it to you again."

"Please do," I mumbled. "I'm still flat broke."

"You see, Adams, you only worked for part of a month in October. Now, that's right, isn't it."

"Yeah, I started on October 20th," I replied.

"Now, like I told you when you phoned in here, whining and crying the last time, it takes a month to set up everything to process your first cheque. Your first full month was November."

"Yeah, so where's my cheque?" I asked.

"Everything will be processed now, and you should get your first cheque around the end of December."

"December," I howled. "What am I supposed to live on until the end of December? How will I ever pay this ruddy gas bill."

"You can always go back and talk to the bank manager," came the calming voice.

"I've already tried that," I grumbled. "It seems that someone's reputation beat me to his door. He's probably still lying on the floor laughing from my last visit. And listen, before you hang up, I've got this other little problem."

"You tell me what it is son and I'll see if it's something I can help," he replied.

"It's my binoculars. There something wrong with the lenses," I informed him.

"The binoculars I gave you?" he asked.

"That's right, the binoculars you gave me," I confirmed. "There's something wrong with them."

"There's nothing wrong with those binoculars," he said. "Those are good binoculars: they're working fine."

"Well, they're not working fine. In fact, they're not working at all. They're all wonky and I can't get them to focus," I said.

"Time, son. Time," he responded in a fatherly way. "You just have to take a little time and learn how to use them, that's all. You work with them and I'm sure you'll figure out how to use them," he said.

"Yeah, okay. I'll work with them. So, anyway, about my cheque. You're telling me I won't get paid now until the end of December?"

"Well, actually Adams, this is your lucky day, or

month I should say," replied the voice of one of the Powers-that-be.

"And just how do you figure that?" I asked.

"Well, Adams, this is December and monthly paycheques always come out before Christmas. I figure you should get your money, oh, I'd say around the 20th of the month. I've got to run now." It was the last thing I heard before the "click" indicating our conversation was over.

"Yes sir, this is my lucky day all right. I'm a three-badge Assistant Conservation Officer, I've got no uniform, but I've got an old green beater of a station wagon, a pair of wonky binoculars and of box of shells." I mumbled. "Now, if the IGA has sardines on sale this week and if Mom has 150 dollars, and if I can find a place, to rent, with a furnace that doesn't drink gas like a camel drinks water, then I've got it made. Why, I might even be able to afford to keep this job."

TRICKS OF THE TRADE

"Whoa," I scolded myself as I jammed on the brakes. Prairie dust billowed up around my green station wagon and slowly drifted down the coulee. I watched as it floated down, engulfing the car parked below me on the slope. I could barely make out the driver of the vehicle and he never moved, when the dust overtook him or when it wafted away. I never took my eyes off the car as I put the green station wagon in reverse and slowly backed out of the coulee. I inched my way back over the ridge and out of sight.

With my fabulous voice, I had been singing a boisterous version of "Big Bad John" when I burst over the rim of the coulee and almost ran into the parked car. If I was going to be a fish cop, I knew I was going to have to be a little more careful in the future. I picked up my issue binoculars, the ones that had been loaned to Noah when he finished the Ark, then carefully opened the door of the green station wagon and stepped out onto the prairie. I hunkered down and pussyfooted my way back to the edge of the coulee.

I picked a spot where I could just see the vehicle and the driver. I lay down on the grass and raised my binoculars. I cursed as I closed one eye to peer through the left lens. But it was no good: everything was so fuzzy, I couldn't tell what he was doing. It did appear though that he was so intent on watching the coulee that he hadn't seen me or noticed the dust bath I had just given him.

There was no doubt in my mind that the guy in the car was concentrating pretty hard, staring into the barren coulee bottom. He was probably part of a hunting party, and his buddies were pushing the coulee. I could wait until the rest of his group appeared. I sat back and I waited and I watched. I didn't want to spoil his hunt. I was in no hurry. When the time was right, I'd have a little chat with him.

In the distance, I heard sounds, many sounds. The sounds of the prairie on a warm, sunny fall day. The wind gently whispering through the short prairie grass. The sounds of geese cackling overhead drew my attention to the skies. I had never seen so many geese in my life – there were thousands upon thousands of them. Flock after flock passed by, many of them directly overhead, right over me and the guy in the car. They circled over the river valley before dropping out of sight beyond the breaks.

Somewhere in the distance, from the coulees and the valley of the Red Deer River, came the unmistakable report of a rifle. I quickly returned my attention to the car. But it did not appear that either the geese or the rifle shots had any effect on the guy.

From my position on the top of the coulee, I also had a pretty good view of the surrounding countryside. The normally quiet prairie was a beehive of activity on this fine day. In a distant coulee I watched a nice buck slowly pick his way to the crest, then bounce away across the prairie. I saw a number of mule deer suddenly burst from out of the next coulee. They paused, looked back, then bounced away like a bunch of rubber balls. If the guy had parked in the next coulee, his partners would have driven the deer right to him. He was too far down the slope and he couldn't see the deer that came bouncing out. He's probably lost and parked in the wrong coulee, I chuckled to myself.

I saw many deer and I saw many vehicles, but I never did see a hunter walking. Vehicles would seem to appear from nowhere, moving slowly across the prairie, then they would disappear below the horizon. There were many hunters out on this fine fall day, but most of them, like the guy sitting down in front of me, appeared to be hunting from the comfort of their vehicles.

The thought of giving chase to one of the moving vehicles crossed my mind, but it was a fleeting thought and I quickly dismissed it. In my short tenure, I had learned that the prairie could be deceiving and misleading. It gave the impression that it was table top flat. But it wasn't. I had often felt like I could see forever

43

and that there was nothing between me and the horizon.

Many times I had felt alone on the vast empty prairie that seemed to be devoid of any living thing. Then, as if by some sort of a miracle, a truck or car would rise up from the seemingly flat surface like a phantom emerging from the bowels of the earth. I would watch as it glided slowly across the horizon, drifting along like a shadow, then silently, without so much as a whisper, it would dip and melt from sight. Lost once again in the vastness.

To chase these phantoms, I had learned, was a fruitless exercise, for upon arriving at the site where I thought they should be, I would find nothing. Nothing but the endless short grass, "prairie wool" as it was known to the pioneers, nothing but prairie wool and emptiness. The vehicle would have disappeared. Where was it? It wasn't where it should be. It was like it had vanished into thin air. Then suddenly, there it was, in the distance, on the horizon. Once again it had shown itself, before slowly melting once more into the grassland.

"A guy could go crazy trying to chase cars out here," I muttered to myself, justifying my reason for sitting on this guy.

Every once in a while I would raise the binoculars to my eyes. I would take a gander around, look at the fuzzy countryside and at the blurry guy in the equally blurry car. I cursed each time I looked through those ruddy binoculars. Man, but I hated those glasses. Somehow, somewhere, I had to get rid of those things.

The sound of a motor starting up caught my attention. The guy in the car, in the coulee, had moved, and I was so busy doing nothing, I had missed it. The car began to move away from me. Slowly, he inched his way along, then turned and went up the other side of the coulee. He seemed to be abandoning his post before his party arrived.

I leapt to my feet and raced back to my own vehicle. I wasn't nearly as concerned about being quiet this time. I slammed the door, roared the motor and tore off after the suspect. This was one vehicle I knew I could catch up to on the prairie. The suspect vehicle was moving slowly, carefully picking its way past a few rocks and a clump of prickly pear cactus.

We both crested the coulee about the same time and, with all the skill of a seasoned prairie driver, I whipped the green station wagon around in front of him. I cut him off. I didn't even have to motion for him to stop. His eyes just bugged right out of his head when my vehicle suddenly stopped right in front of him. He slammed on his brakes to avoid hitting the front of the green station wagon.

"What the hell do you think you're doing?" roared the enraged driver as he charged out of his car. This guy, fuming mad, was going to put me in my place right quick like. Even though I had not yet received my uniform and was dressed in my civvy clothes, unlike most of the hunters I had met, this guy knew who I was. When he bolted out of his vehicle, you could have knocked me over with a feather. I knew who he was, too. His fish and wildlife officer's uniform made it abundantly clear.

Now, I don't mind saying, this was not one of the better moments in my life. I knew that other officers were working the prairie deer season and I was hopeful that, somewhere out on the prairie, I would meet up with one of them. But this was not the meeting I had imagined. I knew that I was going to have to do a lot of back peddling if I was going to buddy up with this guy and pick up a few tricks of the trade. As mad as he was, I figured I'd be lucky if I survived our chance meeting, let alone the rest of the day.

"Well," I replied a little sheepishly. "I uh ... I'm checking hunters and uh, well, I thought that maybe, by the way you were actin' that you were a hunter."

"Whaddaya mean, I looked like a hunter," he snorted.

"Well," I sort of mumbled. "I've been watching you for quite awhile. The way you sat point in the coulee, staring into the bottom, I sure thought you were a hunter."

"You mean ... you been watching me!" he snorted. "How long you been spying on me, kid?" he demanded.

"I wasn't spying on you," I mumbled. "But, I have been watching you for, oh, I don't know, better'n an hour I guess. Maybe better'n an hour and a half."

"I'll tell you something, boy," he snarled. "I don't like sneaky kids. Do I look like a hunter now?"

Actually, I thought he looked like he was right ticked off more than anything. And, I wasn't sure whether it was because I had been watching him, or because he almost ran into the side of my vehicle.

"Well, I guess you're not a hunter," I mumbled, not wanting to further annoy the only other game warden I was ever likely to see on the prairie. I knew I had better tread carefully, for one never knew: one day this guy could actually be my boss and some of these old boys were rumoured to have memories like elephants.

I didn't know much about this guy, but I found out that he knew a lot about me. Well, probably a lot more about my family and ancestry. He wasted little time in sharing this knowledge with me. It took some time, but he finally settled down and quit cursing the inadequacies and stupidity of youth.

Somehow, during his tirade, the old officer determined that it was lunch time.

"Well, would you look at that," he smiled looking at his watch. "I'll be darned if it isn't lunch time. Time to put the old nose bag on." He turned his back on me, ignoring me completely. He whistled and he hummed as he walked to the back of his car. I followed, but at a safe distance. He popped open the trunk revealing a large wooden box, with a lid. He popped the lid on the box and admired the contents.

"Holy cow," I mumbled as I stepped up for a better look. It appeared like the old officer was planning on being here for a long time. It looked to me like he had a whole kitchen, complete with groceries, in that box. There was a frying pan, a tin plate and a tin cup. Stuck in a slotted rack on the under side of the lid was a knife, a fork, a spoon and a butcher knife. Heck, there was a whole assortment of cutlery up there. There were fresh tomatoes, cucumbers, potatoes and onions. And there were canned goods, pork and beans, salmon, peas, corn, peaches. There was a loaf of bread and even salt and pepper. But there were no sardines. The old officer had enough to feed an army.

"Is that issue?" I asked, not really believing what I was seeing.

"Not likely," snapped the old officer. He dug into his grub box and pulled out an old oilcloth. I jumped back to avoid being stepped on when he suddenly turned and walked to the front of his car. There he carefully spread the cloth on the hood of his car. Then he proceeded to haul out his cache of goodies and arranged them on his table.

"A man can't work on an empty stomach," he sang out, more to himself than to me. Although I didn't appear to exist at that moment, I could see his mood had changed. With the array of food in front of him, the old officer was mellowing.

"That was sure a lot of geese that flew over," I mentioned. Now that the air seemed to be clearing, it seemed to be a good time to make some small talk. I also thought it would be right neighbourly if his planned feast included me.

"Geese? What geese? I didn't see no geese," he snapped, cutting me short. The air hadn't cleared as much as I thought. "I wonder when this outfit is going to start hiring some real men," mumbled the old officer. "Nowadays, they hire all these hotshot kids that don't know from nothin'. I get sick and tired of the way they

48

sneak around, prying into other folk's affairs. And they're always looking for a handout, trying to learn the tricks of the trade the easy way." The old officer was having a real good conversation, but not with me. It seemed that the old officer preferred to talk to himself. "Kids nowadays gotta learn they haveta stand on their own two feet."

I slunk back to the station wagon and reached for my grub box. Well, actually, mine was a grub bag. A brown paper grub bag. If I had the slightest thought about sharing his table, it quickly vanished with an icy stare. It was obvious, even to a young officer like myself, that the old officer and I would be dining together, in the open, on separate vehicles. I certainly didn't want to offend him any more than I already had, so I spread out my lunch on the green station wagon. I didn't have an oilcloth, but I didn't need one. In fact, I didn't even need the hood: the fender would do just fine – it provided ample room to accommodate my fare. I barely got started with my lunch when the old officer broke the silence.

"What in the hell's that stink," roared the old officer.

"What stink," I asked. I lifted my nose to test the wind to see if I could identify the offensive odour he was talking about. "I don't smell anything."

"Don't tell me you can't smell that?" he moaned. He wrinkled his nose and squinted his eyes as he searched the countryside. Then he took a look at my table and he stopped. He got the weirdest look on his face.

"What in the hell are you eating, boy," he asked.

"These," I asked, looking at the can and the little

49

silver beauties that were snuggled inside, fin to fin. "These are sardines. Haven't you ever eaten sardines?"

"Not that I'll admit to," he snapped. But curiosity got the better of him and he took a step closer to the station wagon and looked at my lunch. "Sardines and bread! Is that what you're eating?" he asked disgustedly.

"I have to admit, your spread looks much more tempting, but there's nothing wrong with sardines and bread when you're still waiting for your first paycheque," I replied.

"If that's what you're eating kid, you keep your distance. I sure don't want you breathing on me," he snorted and backed away. "And hurry up and eat those damn things or get them out of my sight. You're stinking up the whole countryside."

I picked up my brown paper bag, my loaf of bread and my can of sardines and slunk around to the driver's side of the green station wagon. I put my lunch on the driver's seat, then made sure the windows were all rolled up before I closed the door. With my lunch – the source of the offensive smell – out of the way, I returned to the front of my vehicle. I leaned on the hood and watched hungrily as the old officer put the finishing touches to his meal.

After several minutes of silence the old officer wiped the last crumb from his face. Once more, I tried to make conversation with him. I was still hoping that we could work together for the rest of the day and I could learn from his years of experience. I did not want to upset him further, so I spoke softly.

"There's sure a lot of hunters around," I said.

"Hunters?" he replied curtly. Then he looked around the countryside. At that minute, there was not a car or a red shirt in sight, only the empty prairie. "I haven't seen any." The sharp reply cut off any further conversation.

Then, the old officer began to hum. Each item that he had removed from his grub box, and had not eaten, was picked up from the table cloth. He thoroughly examined each one. Then he cleaned the utensils, wiping each and polishing it until it shone in the noonday sun. He examined each item of food and wrapped it. Then each item was returned to its proper place in his grub box and he closed the trunk lid. He had hummed and ignored me through the whole ritual. When he had finished, I dared another question.

"Do you think we should concentrate our efforts for the rest of the day?" I asked. I was still hoping that I could work with him.

"What? Work together? I should have known there was reason you been hanging around me," he snorted. "Look around you, boy. Do you see anything. Look, it's like a morgue out here. There's nobody around. That's a good one though, concentrating our effort. No, boy, I don't think we'll be concentrating anything." He shook his head as if he couldn't believe what he'd just heard.

He left no doubt when he started his vehicle and drove slowly across the prairie that the old officer and the kid would be going separate ways.

I watched the dust lazily rising from the tires. His car crept up a distant rise then disappeared from sight.

When there was only a hint of dust remaining on the horizon, I walked back to the driver's side of my vehicle.

"C'mon boys," I called to the can of sardines. "Time for lunch. He's gone now."

I flattened the brown paper bag on the hood of the green station wagon. I set the can on top of the brown paper bag and took out a slice of bread. I finished the sardines and I sopped up the last of the oil with a slice of bread.

When I finished eating, I began to hum. I thoroughly examined the remainder of the loaf of bread and carefully returned it to the brown paper bag before I stowed it safely in its proper place – the front seat. Then I flipped the sardine can into the back of the green station wagon. I started the motor and slowly drove off across the prairie.

The finer tricks of the trade were not lost on me.

THE PRAIRIE DUGOUT

I was traveling south of Jenner when a movement out on the prairie caught my eye. A small herd of antelope had burst over the top of a small hill about a half mile off the road and were running like the wind. I slammed on the binders and grabbed my wonky binoculars. The antelope were tightly bunched, in a small group and, even through the fuzzy lenses, I could make out the buck. He was a dandy, a real good one and he was running in the center of the herd. Down the side of the hill they raced. Their mouths were wide open, their tongues hanging out. They were running for their lives, like they were being chased by the devil himself. They seemed to drop into a dip in the prairie and disappeared from sight.

I put the glasses down and scanned the countryside trying to see what had spooked the herd. Then over the hill came the culprit, a truck with a camper streaked into view and raced along the hillside. It was obvious to me, this late in the week of antelope season, that someone had not got their animal. Spotting the herd, the chase was on.

Then came a third object: dark and bouncing like crazy, it was following close on the heels of the truck. I grabbed for the binoculars again. With the aid of the binoculars, I picked up the third object. The wonky lenses made it appear that the truck was being chased by a fuzzy tire. I watched as the truck and the tire rolled out of sight, following in the footsteps of the fleeing herd.

Suddenly, the herd of antelope appeared on another slope. Up the slope they charged until they reached the crest. They lacked only wings to fly as they darted across the skyline, then once more raced into another dale and were gone from sight. The antelope had not lost any steam. They were really pickin' 'em up and puttin' 'em down as they fled.

Sure enough, it wasn't long before the truck, still hot on the trail of the fleeing herd, popped into view. This time, with the aid of the wonky binoculars, I noticed movement near the back of the camper. It was the door. The camper door was open and it was flapping in the breeze. Suddenly it looked like a box jumped right out of the open door. On contact with the ground, the box exploded like a bomb. An assortment of items, probably cans, flew in every direction. Then, the truck disappeared over the hill, still on the heels of the antelope.

I looked back down the hill, looking for the runaway tire. Somewhere in the little valley the tire must have spun out, for it was no longer bouncing after the departing truck.

Once more the antelope shot into view on a distant rise before disappearing. I waited for the truck and I waited for the truck, but it never appeared.

I decided that it would be interesting to talk to the driver of that truck. He shouldn't be too hard to find – all I had to do was follow the trail from the innards of the camper. I looked down the fence line and found a gate. Then I drove out onto the prairie.

I picked up the trail at the deserted tire. A roll of toilet paper strung across a valley, marked the way to a gunny sack. About fifty pounds of spuds were strewn across the prairie. Beside the busted box, I found a loaf of bread, still intact. There were cans strewn about, cans of all types, cans of pork and beans, cans of creamed corn, cans of peas. The bottle of ketchup had not fared too well. It was shattered in a million pieces and the prairie there was stained bright red. The bottle of mustard had added a yellow touch where its contents had spewed forth. There was a sleeping bag all rolled up and tied, impaled in a clump of prickly-pear cactus. A couple of blankets were stretched out on the grass and, further along, a pillow.

A shiny object up ahead caught the sun: it was a crescent wrench, the first of the many tools that adorned the trail.

At the top of the rise, I hit the brakes. There before me, at the bottom of the dip, was a mirage. No, after a good look, I could see it was really two people. Actually it was two men, with their shirts off, standing in water. It was either a prairie slough or a shallow dugout as both were only ankle deep. Both were waving their shirts.

"Hey. Down here. Help," came their frantic screams.

I started up again, driving slowly, following the truck tracks toward the two shirt wavers. The tracks led right to the edge of the water, then disappeared. I drove up to the edge and got out of my green station wagon. It looked as if the two had been having a water fight. Both were soaking wet.

"Hey, man, are we glad to see you," yelled one of the men standing in the water.

"Hi, fellas," I called back. "Say, you fellas didn't happen to see a herd of antelope go scooting through here, followed by a low flying truck, did you?"

They both looked at each other.

"Are you hunting antelope?" asked the talker.

"Nope," I replied. "I'm checking hunters. You guys wouldn't happen to be hunters, would you?"

"Not right now we're not," replied the talker. He looked at me for a second, then asked. "Who are you, anyway?"

"I'm a fish and wildlife officer," I replied proudly. "And I'm hot on the trail of this truck that I saw chase a herd of antelope through here."

"You're a game warden?" he asked, shaking his head. "I don't believe it. You don't look like any game warden I've ever seen."

"Believe it. I'm a game warden," I replied. It was a

ridiculous situation to be in I thought to myself. Here I was a bona fide Assistant Conservation Officer, I had a badge, a beater of an old green station wagon, a pair of wonky binoculars and a box of shells, but no uniform. How did the Powers-that-be expect a man to do enforcement work in a pair of jeans and a baseball jacket. I cursed the time it was taking to get my uniform and the division for their tardiness, as I turned my attention back to the two in the water.

"Now, you're sure you didn't see any antelope or a truck go flying by here?"

"No, I didn't see anything. Did you?" the talker asked his partner.

"Me? No, I didn't see nothing either."

"You guys sure?" I asked. "You know, I could have sworn those antelope ran right through this little swale. You're sure you didn't see them?"

"I'm sure," replied the talker.

"Then, I don't suppose you saw the truck that was chasing them either?"

Again they looked at each other. "Truck?" he replied. He took on a look that was supposed to show shock and surprise. Then he shook his head. "No, I never seen a truck either. Did you see a truck go by here?" he asked his partner.

"Nope. I never saw a truck either," said the partner.

"I was sure they came right over the top of that rise," I replied and pointed back in the direction I came from. " I'd have thought the antelope would have been close enough for you reach out and touch. In fact, judging from the tracks, the truck must have run right over top of you."

"You must have been mistaken," replied the talker. "We've been here all morning and haven't seen a soul. You're the first living thing we've seen and are we ever glad to see you." They were pretty cool dudes. Albeit, wet cool dudes.

"Oh, I don't think I was mistaken," I replied confidently. "You know, those guys that were chasing those antelope, I'd say they must have been in one heck a hurry when they took off after them."

"Why's that?" asked the talker.

"Why?" I chuckled. "Why, because they left quite a trail across the prairie."

"Yeah? What kind of trail?"

"Oh, you know, the usual stuff that vehicles chasing antelope leave. A tire, groceries, sleeping bags, tools, you know, stuff like that. You could call it camping stuff I guess."

"I thought you said you closed the door?" the talker said to his partner. The tone in his voice sounded like he was about to lose his cool.

"I did," replied the partner defensively.

"Did you lift the tailgate?"

"Oh, oh," moaned the partner. "I think so, but I don't remember."

"Now, are you guys sure you didn't see that herd of antelope?" I asked again.

"No, we're sure," replied the talker.

"Okay then, I'll see you later," I replied. I started to get back into the green station wagon.

"Wait up, just a minute there. Where do you think

you're goin'?" called the talker excitedly.

"Me," I replied. "Well, if it's all right with you boys, I'm going to try and find the guys that were chasing that herd of antelope. After all, I am a fish and wildlife officer, remember. That's what I do for a living."

"Well, because … hey, c'mon man, you're not just gonna leave us out here, alone, are you?"

"I sure am," I laughed. "There's no law against parking your truck in a dugout and there's no law against standing on top of your truck in a dugout. Why, you two can stand in a dugout all day. In fact, you can even stand on the top of your truck in a dugout all day, if you want. But, there is a law about chasing antelope and I have to find the lawbreakers. Now, if you two were the antelope chasers, I'd probably be able to help you out, after I gave you the appropriate tickets."

Neither man spoke.

I climbed into the green station wagon and drove over the hill, in the same direction the antelope had disappeared. I left the two water babies, standing ankle deep in the prairie dugout, on the roof of their truck with the open tail gate.

VENISON STEAKS

It was deer season on the Alberta prairies, my first since joining Fish & Wildlife less then a month earlier. The very thought of deer brought back many mouth-watering memories.

"Oh, I'd never pass up a deer," Dad would always say whenever he was asked about his favorite game. And Dad was right, for I would be hard pressed to find anything that tasted better then a venison steak. I could almost taste the delicious little deer chops that were dancing in my head.

"What I wouldn't give right now for a fried venison steak," I said, out loud, to myself. "Oh, man, even a cold one. One of Mom's canned venison steaks would be a welcome change to the boys in the can." I was of course referring to the cans of sardines that were destined to be my lunch, supper and probably midnight snack if I stayed out on the prairie long enough.

But venison steak was not on the menu, or even in the foreseeable future. Since joining Fish & Wildlife, the only venison steaks I had seen were in my dreams. The real thing, the sardines, the things that dreams were definitely not made of, were in the brown paper bag on the seat beside me. Today, like every other day, I would dine on sardines and bread. Maybe next year there would be venison steaks, I consoled myself.

It was November, and I was working an area that had become my favorite haunt, the coulees and breaks along the Red Deer River north of Brooks. The morning sun was slowly burning the chill off what promised to be a beautiful day. And, on this beautiful day, there were hunters everywhere. Everywhere I looked I saw red coats, cars and pick-up trucks. For some reason, it seemed like every-where there were hunters, there were illegal deer.

The thought of fresh deer steaks was still vivid in my mind when I stopped to check the first vehicle. I stopped, downwind of course, to avoid giving the boys a dust bath. Out of the green station wagon into the dust and the prairie breeze I strode. I halted immediately, for there was more then dust that swirled about me. Floating on the prairie breeze was a distinct odor. A rotten odor. But the boys, dressed in red, were in a joyful mood, oblivious to the dust or the odor and they hastily called me over. I hesitated, for a second, checking the air. The stink had to be coming from somewhere.

This group of hunters didn't know me from Adam, but they couldn't wait to show me their prize.

"Look at this beauty," one proud nimrod called as he popped open the trunk revealing a huge mule deer buck and the most putrid smell that one man ever told another about. The big buck was well into the rut, and his neck was swollen, puffed out like a giant over-stuffed sausage. And stink? That buck stunk to high heaven. From the tip of his nose to the end of his tail he stunk. I could feel my stomach begin to heave as I hastily backed away from the car.

"Now, I ask you, sir, ain't that a beauty?" asked one of the guys proudly. "You ever see a buck that big in all your life?"

"Can't say as I've seen one that was that big, or one that smelled that bad," I replied. "What are you gonna do with it now?"

"What're we gonna do with? We're gonna eat it."

"You're gonna eat that thing," I replied. "Did you guys even bother to dress it?"

"You bet," replied one of the occupants. "We field dressed it. Why?"

"Why," I repeated. "Because, I never smelled anything like that in my life. That's why."

"That's just the way a good buck smells," he said. "Big bucks always smell a little when they're in rut. I bet there's gonna be a lot of flavor in that meat."

"I think you can bet on that all right," I agreed. "Man, I don't know how you can stand it. I think I'd be sick if I had to ride around with that thing all day."

"Only guys who can't shoot a big deer like that, don't like the smell," he laughed. "Where's your deer?" he asked and at the same time gave the green station wagon a good look. "I don't see your deer anywhere? What's the matter, you can't hit one?"

"No, I'm not hunting. But, if you don't mind, I'd like to see your licences and tags?" I asked. What I really wanted to do was just get away from the smell.

"Why do you want to see our licences and tags?" he asked.

"Because I'm a fish and wildlife officer," I informed him.

"A what?" he asked, and a look of surprise, then shock, came over his face. Reluctantly, he and his partners handed me their licences and tags. All of them, all of the licences and all of the tags. Even the tag that should have been on the big stinking Mule Deer buck. The buck didn't have a tag on it. The first thing a hunter must do after killing an animal is place his tag on it. It should have been done, but it wasn't and, now, I had to seize the stinking deer. I was the possessor of this vile-smelling thing.

It was the first deer I had ever picked up and I was very diligent in preserving and caring for this exhibit. I knew I had to protect and preserve the evidence until after the court case. Because, when this thing was over, someone, who I did not know, certainly not me, would be eating deer steaks. Why anyone would want to eat this stinking deer was beyond me.

Too proud to ask for help, I grunted and groaned and held my breath as I wrestled the deer out of their trunk. I jumped back, to avoid the blood that splattered onto the grass when the carcass hit the ground. Grasping the big buck by the antlers I dragged it across the prairie to the green station wagon. I hoisted the head and antlers up and into the back of the station wagon. But the swollen neck and the body, the really heavy parts, stuck to the prairie ground like glue. I crawled over the head and antlers into the back of the station wagon and crouching low, tried to pull the beast in. No luck; there was too much resistence. It appeared that the big stinking buck did not want to ride with me.

Back over the head and antlers I scrambled out onto the prairie grass once more and surveyed the scene. The unamused hunters watched quietly. Grabbing the big buck around the ribs, just behind the front legs, I gave a mighty heave, lifted up and pushed at the same time. The carcass moved, it was a little closer to being loaded.

Then I felt it. On the front of my pants, running down my legs, a warm wet feeling. The buck's blood was oozing out onto my clothes. I dropped the big buck like I had just been stung and stared down. The part of the big buck that was in the trunk fell back and flopped onto the prairie grass. Blood splattered, on the ground, on the grass, on my shoes and on my pants. I was now soaked in blood.

The unamused hunters were now quite amused and they laughed heartily.

Undeterred by a little blood, I accepted the minor setback and with more determination than ever I tackled the job again. I was not sure at times who was being loaded, me or the big buck. At times I was on top pushing and pulling; other times I was on the bottom, pushing and pulling. Persistence did win out and eventually I succeeded. I now stunk as bad as the big buck that lay in the green station wagon. There, at least the meat would be spared a coating of prairie dust protecting the meat and the ever present stench.

By the time I left the scene, I was covered in blood from the top of my head to the soles of my feet. I was sure there was no more blood left in the big buck: it was all on me.

I rolled the windows up tight to prevent the dust from rolling in, but I couldn't keep the sun out and the temperature was rising in the green station wagon as I drove off across the prairie. Oh, man, was it rising. As the sun climbed high in the sky, the temperature rose sky high on the inside of the green station wagon. And that was not all that was rising. That stinking mule deer buck was now steaming like a boiling kettle and the smell on the inside of the vehicle was rising. It was reaching proportions I had never dreamed of. It was enough to gag a maggot.

In the back, I heard the rattle of empty sardine cans. Even they can't stand the smell, I thought. They're probably falling over each other trying to get out for a breath of fresh air. I never thought it would happen, but I was beginning to long for the comfortable stench that had occupied the old green station wagon when I first inherited it.

In the sweltering heat and the gut-wrenching stench, I was beginning to have a healthy appreciation for just how smart Dad really was. Back on the stump farm, we had eaten a lot of deer meat. Mule deer meat that was fresh, fried, roasted, cold and canned, but never, ever, had any of it smelled like this. But then, Dad was a meat hunter and he hunted solely for food. Dad was never one to shoot big bucks. Sitting in the heat and the stink, I could hear him: it was just like he was sitting next to me.

"Them horns make mighty thin soup, son," Dad had often said. Dad always preferred to shoot a dry doe, sometime in the late summer, when they were well fed and nice and fat. Yes, before I encountered this group I could have eaten a nice deer steak. Now, I was having some serious doubts.

My stomach had not stopped retching from the time I smelled the big mule deer buck. What was left of my breakfast had been doing speed laps around my stomach and now I could taste it in my throat. Finally, I could take it no more. I jammed on the brakes and bailed out of the green station wagon. I raced away, upwind, away from the station wagon, away from the stench. There, alone on the prairie, I leaned over with my hands on my knees, but I could not escape the smell. It was imbedded in my blood-soaked clothing. While I gasped for fresh air, my breakfast kept making runs up and down my throat, trying to escape.

I was so busy trying to be sick, I didn't even hear the vehicle drive up. A group of hunters, thinking I was one of them, thought I was a hunter in distress. They had raced across the prairie to lend a helping hand. It was a bad error in judgement on their part. They had no idea that the sickly green guy with the green station wagon was a green game warden. The deer they had hoisted and displayed like a trophy on top of their vehicle was not sporting the required tag. Unhappily, they too contributed their deer to the cause. Even in my sickly state, I could not bring myself to ask for assistance when I began the task of removing the deer from their vehicle.

"Whoa," yelled one of the hunters. He got pretty excited when I grabbed the most accessible part, a hind leg. I was about to reef the critter off the top of his vehicle. "Wait, we'll help you with that."

"Don't worry, I've done this before," I assured him.

"That may be so," he replied unhappily. "But not on my vehicle you haven't. You just stand back and we'll get it off."

"Whatever," I said and stepped back.

Carefully, under the guidance of the owner, the crew lifted the animal. One guy grabbed the front legs, the owner the hind legs. The third guy had the tough job: he had to reach up for the head and antlers.

"You be careful now and watch them horns," cautioned the owner. "They can raise hell with the paint."

Ever so gently, the animal was hoisted up and off the roof. Not so much as a hoof or tine touched the paint. Then they dumped the carcass like a sack of garbage on the prairie grass. Then I had a wonderful thought. I knew there was no room in the green station wagon with the big buck already in there. This one would have to go on the roof rack and since these guys had been so helpful I decided now was a good time to ask for help.

"Hey fellas, you're not finished yet," I chuckled. "I'd

appreciate it if you'd pick it up and throw it onto the station wagon."

"Pick it up yourself and throw it where ever you want," replied the owner. "We shot it for you. Now if you want it, you load it. You're probably gonna take it home and eat it anyway."

"Me?" I asked. "Me eat this. Why guys, that would be illegal."

"I'll bet," he snorted. The trio stood back and watched.

Now I had two deer: one big smelly one in the station wagon, one little one on the ground. And, once again, I had an audience. If I had used my head – but that was still clogged with of the smell of the big stinking rutting mule deer buck – I would have chosen the inside of the green station wagon instead of the top. It would have been much easier to drag it into the back and throw it on top of the first, but, oh no, thinking the back of the station wagon was full, I had to do it the hard way. I chose the top, and if I thought I had worked loading the first deer, I couldn't have been more mistaken. Loading the big buck had been a breeze; loading the second was a horrible gut-wrenching experience in front of a critical, hostile audience.

I lifted, I pushed and I pulled, but getting a deer up onto the top of the green station wagon was a task considerably greater then getting one into it. Some part of the carcass always seemed to have a mind of its own and would not follow the rest.

I really worked up a sweat, but I gave it my all. There was no way I was going to fail, not in front of the audience. Silently, to myself, I grunted and groaned, I even threw in a few curse words to help. Had I cursed out loud, the words would have blended right in with those I was getting from the boys.

Strange, I thought, how quickly people can change. They had been so helpful when they first arrived and didn't know who I was. Now that they knew, they were just hateful, cursing individuals. One even suggested that it would be poetic justice if I fell off the green station wagon and broke my neck.

Finally, I was successful in getting the antlers hooked over the top of the roof rack. Then I climbed on top and pulled, straining, sweating and cursing, until I succeeded in wrestling the second deer onto the top of the green station wagon, without any help. Now, I was ready to leave the boys.

Inside the green station wagon it was even hotter, more putrid and smellier then before. It was a hell hole. As much as I wanted to get away from the boys, I couldn't take the stench any more. I had to get out one more time. I opened the tailgate and rolled down the windows. If I was going to survive this day, I desperately needed some air.

I hadn't driven far when I realized that leaving the tailgate down was not such a good idea. As I drove across the dry prairie grass, dust that had lain on the prairies all summer rose up from the tires. It swirled in a huge cloud around the back of the green station wagon, then funneled in. It was only minutes before there was more dust inside the green station wagon than there was outside. Trying to look through the windshield was worse than looking through a dense fog, and breathing was almost impossible. Unfortunately, the boys were not yet out of sight before I had to stop. Gagging and choking, I stumbled from the green station wagon and groped my way around to the back and closed the tailgate. From afar, laughter echoed and drifted across the prairie.

I stood out on the prairie for a few seconds to get a little fresh air. The sun was due south and I realized that it was lunchtime. I paused a moment as I thought of the tasty little silver fellas that awaited me. But, try as I might, I could not bring myself to eat. I had no stomach for food, let alone a can of oily sardines.

Some days never seem to end and this was one of those days. After picking up the second deer, I had only one thought. Get back to Brooks and get that stinking buck out of my station wagon. But a hasty return to the bright lights was not in the stars. It seemed to me that every illegal hunter in the world had descended on the little patch of prairie where I was patrolling.

I had been wrong about the inside of the station wagon being full with only the big buck in it. During the course of the day, I had crawled over and around that buck a half a dozen times as I pushed and crammed one deer after another into it. When I finished, it was full: from the floor to the roof, from one side to the other, there was no more room for deer.

"Oh, no," I moaned when I stood back. The green station wagon looked like a gut wagon. The inside of the windows were streaked with blood and matted with hair. I shuddered at the thought of the blood seeping out of those carcasses and dripping onto the floor. No wonder the inside stunk so bad, I thought. I could only shake my head when I thought of the cleaning task that lay ahead. I knew I could never get all of the blood out. The stink would be there forever.

When the inside was full, I had to crawl back onto the top of the green station wagon. I pushed and pulled deer onto the roof rack until it, too, was loaded to capacity. Blood dripped from the animals and ran from the roof. Streaks of blood adorned the sides and back of the green station wagon. If the stink wasn't bad enough, the blood-streaked windshield was a constant reminder of my load. Gobs of hair were pasted all over the car. The only space left in the green station wagon was on the passenger's seat, next to me, and I refused to share the streaked view. I turned a blind eye to the hunting fraternity. There would be no more deer.

Finally, around suppertime, I pulled up at the back of the Brooks IGA. It was the only place in town where I could take animals and have them properly cared for and processed.

"Hi," I greeted the butcher when I hauled myself, caked from top to bottom with dried blood, through the back door. "I've got some deer for you."

He stood and stared at me for several seconds before he spoke. "What have you been doing, man?" he asked, and his eyes said he did not really believe what he saw.

"Checking hunters," I replied. "What does it look like?"

"I've never seen anything like that in my life," he

laughed. "What did you do, find a puddle of blood and roll in it?"

"Looks bad, doesn't it?" I replied.

"It looks worse then that," he assured me.

"Anyway, I got some deer for you. Where do you want them?"

"I don't, he replied. "I've already cleaned up the machines. I'm not going to mess this place up for one deer. I'm finished for the day."

"How about two deer?" I asked.

"Two deer." he thought about that for a moment. "Naw, I don't think so," he replied. "However, if you had more than …."

"You've got yourself a deal," I replied happily. "Man, have I got more. C'mon outside and I'll help you unload them."

I don't think he was all that happy to see my load. "What in the name of …, " he whistled when he saw the green station wagon. "What's going on, anyway?"

"Beats me," I replied. "I've never seen anything like it. It's crazy out there. It seemed like every group I checked had an illegal deer. "

"What's that smell?" he asked turning up his nose.

"What smell?" I asked. I lifted my nose to the wind and took a deep breath.

"Can't you smell that," he snorted. "It smells like there's something rotten out here."

"You might be smelling the big buck," I replied. "He's a little high, but not that bad," I lied.

"Well, I suppose I can take them, but I'm not taking that thing that's stinking."

"You gotta," I said, pleading with him. "I have to preserve the evidence for court."

"I don't know about that," he replied hesitantly. "Why don't we get the rest unloaded and then I'll have a look at it. But, I can tell you right now, I can't have something like that smelling up my beef."

"Don't worry. It's not really all that bad," I lied again. "It'll be okay. Once you get it cut up and frozen you won't even notice the smell," I assured him.

The last animal to be unloaded was, of course, the big buck. Deer seized later in the day had been stacked around and on top of him. The aroma surrounding him had not diminished during the day. In fact, if anything, it had risen to greater heights.

"Oh, my lord," moaned the butcher when we dragged the big buck out of the back. "Did you drive around with this thing inside all day."

"All day," I replied.

"I can't believe it," he said, shaking his head. "I can't believe it."

"Yeah, well, believe it," I said. The stench was still bad enough to knock a skunk off a gut wagon. "Actually, you don't even notice it after awhile."

"I don't believe that, either," he said.

"Well, that makes you a really smart man," I replied.

The butcher was busy checking each animal. When he got to the big buck, he stopped. "Did you check this one closely?" he asked.

"Yeah. Why?"

"C'mere, look at this," he said. "It's only half dressed."

"What do you mean 'only half dressed?'" I asked.

"Look. See that? That's the diaphragm. The vital organs are still in it."

I looked, and, sure enough, the diaphragm was still there. That meant the heart, lungs and liver were still inside. "So that's field dressed, is it?" I asked.

"What do you mean, field dressed?" asked the butcher. "I never heard of anything called 'field dressed.'"

"Me neither, but when I checked these guys this morning, they said they had field dressed the deer. I guess that's what they meant by field dressed."

"What do you want me to do with it?" he asked.

"Same as the rest," I replied. "With any luck, they'll get it back and have to eat it. Now, wouldn't that be justice."

"Would you eat it?" he asked.

"Me. Not on your life," I replied. Then I looked down at the caked blood, mucus and deer hair on my body. "I'll never eat mule deer again."

OPEN WATER

"Hang on to your fur hat, Charlie," I yelled. Then I took a quick glance at Charlie, my passenger, as the back end of the old green station wagon started to swing out. It was getting ready to pass the front end. Charlie, the old fishery officer, had already gritted his teeth. Both of his weathered hands were clamped firmly on the dash board. Charlie was ready for the worst.

It was late March, and the commercial fishery on Lake Newell was coming to an end. Charlie and I were out on the lake on a bright sunny afternoon checking fishermen. Although the snow was gone and the ice appeared to be clear and smooth as glass, it was deceiving.

The surface was not as frozen as it appeared. Here and there, thin layers of surface water lay on top of the ice and net holes were everywhere. Many of the holes were wide open, and some greatly enlarged from the surface water running into them. All were very difficult to see. On the north end of the lake, a couple of large pressure ridges had formed, pushing ice several feet in the air. Along the pressure ridges, there were open water leads.

It was a gorgeous day. I had guided the green station wagon around the holes and followed the route others had taken, through a gap in the ridges. The pressure ridges were far behind us, out of sight, when Charlie and I stopped near a gang of nets on the west side of the lake to have lunch. Suddenly, we heard a tremendous, BOOM. The whole lake seemed to shiver.

"What the hell was that?" I asked Charlie. My eyes quickly searched the area around my feet. I was sure that the ice had given way and I was headed for the bottom of the lake.

"Oh, that's just the ice talking," Charlie replied. He seemed to be unconcerned.

"What does that mean?" I asked. "I never heard of ice talking before."

"By the sound of it, and the way it shook, I'd say the lake heaved and the ice surface split," he replied. Charlie calmly looked around at the ice-covered lake.

I looked too, but I couldn't see anything on the horizon except more ice.

"See anything?" I asked. Man, this was more than a little spooky. I wouldn't mind if the old green station wagon went to the bottom of the lake, but I certainly didn't want to.

"No, I don't see anything," Charlie replied.

"Do you think the crack's headed this way?" I asked.

"If it was, it would have been here by now," Charlie said, and continued to eat his lunch.

"Do you think we should get off the lake, while we still can?" I asked. I wasn't quite as calm as Charlie was. For some reason, I had lost my appetite.

"We can do that," Charlie replied. "We could head on south and get off, then we could pick up the trail and drive around the shoreline and check the fish plants. What do you think?"

"I think we should get off this lake," I replied. "And the sooner, the better."

"Yeah," Charlie chuckled. "We can do that."

One thing about driving on the lake: traveling in any direction is no problem. It's like one super highway and, mostly, there's nothing to run into. The surface on the southern part of the lake was as smooth as glass and it was like driving on a giant mirror. We started out slowly and cautiously, but I was in a hurry to get off the lake, away from the big boom. I kept pushing the accelerator a little closer to the floor boards.

"I think I'd be inclined to take it a little slower," Charlie said. It was his polite way of telling me to slow down. I liked Charlie.

"Yeah," I replied. Charlie was cautious, but this was not my first time on the lake. I knew what I was doing. Slowly, I pushed the pedal down another notch. We were cruising along at a pretty good clip – between 50 - 60 mph – when the back wheels decided to take the lead.

"Be careful," Charlie cautioned me.

But it was too late.

"Whoa," I yelled as the back wheels took the lead. Charlie and I were both looking back to the spot where we had lunch, but for only a second. The old green station wagon was heading for the south end of the lake, spinning like a top. As the horizon spun around us, I forgot about the boom.

"Hey, Charlie, isn't this fun?" I asked and I smiled at him.

But, Charlie wasn't amused. There was no smile on his face. There was only a look of sheer terror. The car was spinning wildly, but Charlie's head was spinning even faster, looking from side to side trying to see where we were headed.

"Man, was that fun," I chuckled, when the old green station wagon finally spun to a stop.

Charlie never said a word. He got out onto the ice and looked around. We had come to a stop in surface water. Water stretched as far as we could see, toward the Rainier draw.

"I think this is runoff water," Charlie said. "I don't think it would be wise to go any father south." Charlie looked to the east. I looked to the east. It was a vast sheet of ice with not a sign of anything on the surface. Then Charlie looked to the west. There was surface water covering the ice for a long way, but in the distance there was the shoreline.

"Which way?" I asked.

"I don't know," Charlie replied. I had worked with Charlie all winter, and I hadn't known too much that concerned him. But, today, after the big boom, it looked to me like Charlie was concerned.

"Let's go east," I said. "I think we should be able to see any pressure ridge before we get to it."

"Okay," Charlie replied. "But, I think we should take it a little slower."

"Right," I replied. I turned toward the east and the center of the lake. Before I knew it, I was cruising, eating up the smooth ice.

"I think we should take it a little slower," Charlie said again. I noticed that both his hands were once again gripping the dashboard.

"Hey, Charlie, want to try for one more little spin," I said jokingly. "We could spin the other way, you know, to sort of unwind?"

But Charlie's eyes were fixed on the ice ahead. He didn't see the humour and his face showed it. Charlie was not having a good day as we sped across the center of the lake. I, on the other hand, I was having a great time. I had forgotten about the big boom.

"I think you should slow it down a bit," Charlie said.

"Do you see something?" I asked. I stared at the ice ahead of me, but all I could see was more ice. It all looked the same to me.

"I'm not sure," Charlie replied. "It looks like there could be a little ice ridge just ahead." Charlie was a master at reading the ice. Just a teensy weensy change in colour and Charlie knew what it meant. But not me.

"I don't see, nothing," I replied. But Charlie's words prompted me to sit up and now, I was right up over the steering wheel, peering through the windshield. I took a little pressure off the gas pedal and glanced at Charlie. His face was the colour of snow. I looked back at the ice, but whatever it was that Charlie saw did not stand out for me. I could see a few different shades of blue, on the ice in front of the car, but they were nothing to worry about. After all, blue was blue and there were always a wide range of blues and greens in ice and in the water. It didn't mean a thing.

But Charlie was worried, so I took my foot right off the accelerator and lightly touched the brake to ease his mind. Touching the brakes on the glare ice, made no difference whatsoever in our speed. In fact, it felt like we were speeding up. We certainly hadn't lost any momentum and the car was still hurtling straight for the odd-coloured ice. We were going too fast and it was too late when I could see that Charlie had been right again. The different hue of blue was an ice ridge.

"Whoa," Charlie yelled, when the ridge suddenly jumped up in front of us.

"Hang on," I yelled.

Charlie had a vice-like grip on the dashboard. He was hanging on for dear life.

With a sinking feeling I yelled again. "Hang on, Charlie. We're gonna hit 'er head on." I braced myself for the inevitable. But there was not the violent crash I was expecting. Instead, the car had gone up an incline, a ramp, where the ice had lifted. Instantly, we were airborne. What a neat feeling: it was just like flying, I thought, as the green station wagon sailed up and over the ridge. Just as suddenly, I was brought back to reality as the car came down on the ice several feet past the ridge.

"Should we go back and try it again?" I grinned and looked at Charlie, but Charlie wasn't grinning back. There wasn't even a hint of a smile on his ashen face.

"I think we're lucky to be alive," Charlie said.

"You think so?" I asked. "It was only a very small ice ridge. We could probably bounce right back over it from this side."

"We're lucky we didn't land in that open water," replied a very sober Charlie.

I looked back at the ice ridge, and dark bluish line that stretched along the east side of the ridge. The dark bluish line, the open water.

"Holy cow, I didn't even see that," I replied and my knees started to shake. "Did you know that water was there?" I asked.

"I did when we were flying over it," he replied.

"I wonder how wide it was."

"I'd say it looked to be about 10, maybe 15 feet across."

"I can't believe you saw that," I said "After we hit the ridge, all I saw was clear blue sky until we landed on the other side."

"I can believe that," Charlie replied. "You think you can slow it down a bit, now," he said. "I think I've had enough thrills for one day."

The ride toward the east shore continued, but at a much slower pace. Finally, the shoreline appeared on the horizon. About the same time, surface water appeared once more on the top of the ice. The closer we got to the east shore the more water we encountered. As the water got deeper, and rose on the tires, I pushed the gas pedal a little closer to the floor.

As the green station wagon picked up speed, the shoreline disappeared behind a wall of water that rose up in front of the car before cascading on the windshield.

Charlie and I could no longer see the nice sunny day and we couldn't see through the windshield. I aimed the car for what I thought should be the shoreline and tramped the gas to the floor. Water was flying in every direction. The windshield wipers were flapping wildly, but they couldn't take it off fast enough. Charlie and I were driving blind, heading for the east shore.

"You're going to kill us," Charlie yelled.

"You want me to slow down?" I called back. Once again I was leaning over the steering wheel. This time I was trying to get a peak through the windshield at anything, anything other than water.

"Not now. Not in water like this," Charlie yelled again. "You better hope you don't kill the engine."

"I hope not," I replied.

"I hope there's no more ridges," he said. Charlie bobbed his head from side to side, up and down, trying to get a look at anything ahead as he peered through the side window. There was no use him looking out the windshield; I was doing that and I was seeing enough of nothing for both of us. "Maybe, if you sort of snake along, I might be able to see through the side window."

"You think there might be more ridges?" I asked.

"I hope not, but there's certainly a pile of net holes

in this area," he replied. "I don't want to hit one of those either."

"You sure you don't want me to slow down?" I asked.

"No. You keep the speed up now as long as you can," he directed.

"I can do that," I replied. "Anything else?" I asked.

"Pray," Charlie said. "Pray."

Suddenly the old green station wagon bounced and the ride got mighty rough. The water stopped and we were racing across the prairie.

"Stop," Charlie yelled. This time I obeyed and slammed on the brakes.

Charlie stepped out of the car as soon as it came to a stop. I don't think he really believed we had made it and he was still alive. I joined him at the back of the green station wagon and we both looked back at the lake.

I watched the ripples from the wake as they flowed away in an ever enlarging "V." We had been very lucky. Even when we hit land we had been lucky, coming ashore at a place where there was not an embankment.

"I guess we'll have to be more careful tomorrow," I said.

"Not me," Charlie replied. "From now on, you're on your own."

"WELL, YOU'RE MISSING 'EM, KID"

The telephone call came on a cloudy day. Just the kind of call a person needs when it appears there is a storm on the horizon.

"Adams," said the caller. It was his only word of greeting. "Are you trying to be funny, boy?"

"What do you mean?" I asked.

"I received this piece of paper titled 'Pheasant Brood Survey'; this thing can't be complete. I hope you're not trying to pull my leg?" asked the voice. It was one of the Powers-that-be.

"That's it," I replied happily. Finally, I thought, someone has acknowledged my work. "And, you'll be pleased to know that I've got a couple more done for you."

"Well, I certainly hope your eyesight was better on the last surveys then it was on the first one," said the unhappy voice.

"What's wrong with it?" I asked. Slowly it was dawning on me that the clouds outside did not signal the only storm that was brewing.

The transects were the 20-mile stretches of road that had been identified for counting pheasants in the Brooks district. There were several of them scattered throughout the district and were identified by the names of the small communities they were near, towns with names like Tilley, Cassils, Rolling Hills, Duchess, Rosemary and Scandia.

I, being the junior man in the district, had drawn the short straw and it was I who was running the transects. One thing that had been drilled into my head when I was with the RCMP was the importance of having a good working relationship with the people in your district. Perception. Relationships. Image. They were important tools for an officer.

For a fish and wildlife officer, the land owners were very important people. They played a major role in the management of wildlife and they were extremely important to a good enforcement program. Yes, the image that an officer portrayed was extremely important, especially in a small town.

Whenever I was out on a transect, I was extremely careful about how I deployed myself. Safety was also a big concern and, every time I had to stop the old green station wagon, I would check the rear view mirror before pulling over to the side of the road. And, sometimes, I'd drive right into the ditch because the transects often followed very narrow roads. I would shut off the motor, get out of the station wagon and close the door. Anyone else using the road would not be impeded by my actions. I still didn't have a uniform, but people were getting to know the green station wagon. Oh yes, the way you went about your business and the way people viewed you was very important. Image and perception were everything.

Transects were run at various times of the year. They were the means by which the biological staff kept track of the pheasant population and one of the methods used for setting the bag limits and the hunting seasons. They were another task totally foreign to a kid from the muskeg of western Alberta, but I had already run several of them.

I did the sex ratio counts in the winter when the snow was on the ground. Along the transect route, I counted every pheasant, male and female. For this job, I needed every piece of issue equipment I had. Well, every piece except the three badges and the box of rifle shells. I could have even used some that I didn't have, like a uniform.

I was keen to get started, but after running a few of the transects I was starting to have mixed feelings, not to mention splitting headaches. I found that being out in the field with birds was to me one of the most enjoyable aspects of the job. But, counting pheasants was a real pain, a pain in the head. I suffered headaches and, by the end of each transect, I had this piercing pain that shot through my right eye and over my forehead before exploding in my head. Then it seemed like this long hand would reach down and grab the muscles in the back of my neck and tie them in a knot.

The culprit, the cause of my pain, was the pair of old beaten-up stomped-on poor excuse for binoculars. Issue binoculars, I had got them right from Edmonton, from the Powers-that-be. A pair of Bushnell, 7 x 35s that I am sure had been issued to someone during the First World War. They had to be war surplus, I thought. How else could they possibly have got all the tell-tale signs of being run over by a tank.

"I don't like to complain all the time, about the equipment I was issued, but these binoculars I was given, they're just no good," I protested to the Powers-that-be whenever I was given the opportunity.

"There's nothing wrong with those glasses," I was advised each time I complained. "The problem is, you young bucks don't appreciate nothing. If you spent as much time learning how to use them as you do whining and crying we'd all be a lot better off."

So I fiddled with the glasses. Sometimes, if I held my mouth just right, I could almost get the left lens to focus. Almost, but not quite. Fuzz, there was always a little bit of fuzz on everything I looked at out of the left lens. Now, the right lens was another story. There was no amount of fiddling or cursing that I could do that would clear up that lens. The right lens would never focus, either by itself or jointly with the left lens. From the right lens, there was only this constant eye-sucking blur.

However, I found that I needed help in finding many of the sneaky hens in the fields and feedlots. The hens had this nasty habit of hunkering down and flattening themselves out, disguising themselves. At a distance, it was only with the assistance of my not so trusty binoculars that I could differentiate some of the birds from the frozen cow-pies.

Maybe the Powers-that-be were right, I thought, as I cruised the roads in search of the pheasant. I had to admit, if I closed my right eye and squinted, just right, I could almost see through the left lens and the image in the distance was brought nearer. The image was never clear, but with a little practice I was able to tell by the amount of fuzz that appeared on the object whether it was a hen or a cow-pie. Pheasants gave off a different sort of fuzzy look than cow-pies.

However, there were times when, in the midst of the excitement of trying to count the many pheasants that appeared, I would foolishly open both eyes. Without thinking, I would then spin the dials, I would have them buzzing like flies around a sugar bowl, trying to focus the lenses.

The result of this momentary lapse of sanity was an excruciating, eye-sucking experience. Not right away, mind you. At first, I wouldn't even notice it. But as the transect and the day wore on, it felt like my right eye-ball had been sucked right out of my head and slammed onto the dashboard.

I cursed those binoculars every time I took them out of their case. After every day's use, I swore, never again, but on the next transect, when a large group of pheasants presented themselves, without thinking, I would grab for the binoculars. Once again my eye-ball was destined to bounce around on the dashboard.

I had run the crowing counts in the spring counting

the roosters along the transect routes. Thankfully, I did not need binoculars to hear a rooster crow.

"The pheasants," said the voice jarring me back to the stormy day. "The pheasants, Adams. Where are they?"

"They're all there," I replied. "I recorded every one, just like I was told."

"Something's missing then. This thing can't be complete," replied the voice, "You're missing too many birds. Are you sure you know what you're looking for?"

"Are you trying to tell me something?" I asked, just a little put out by the tone as the storm clouds grew heavy.

"No. No. I'm not trying to tell you anything. I'm just saying, well, you're missing 'em, kid. This is the worst brood count I've ever seen." There was a long silence. Neither of us said anything. "Look, kid," the voice finally said. "I don't think you know what you're looking for. That's what I'm telling you. Maybe you just need some help until you become a little more familiar with what you're doing. How about we send someone down to work with you for a couple of days. How does that sound?"

"Well, maybe if I had a decent pair of binoculars …" I started to protest, getting my shot in about the state of the equipment, but he cut me off.

"Binoculars have nothing to do with it," he replied.

"Fine then, send someone down," I snorted indignantly.

Next day, just as promised, there was a visitor from headquarters, a man more experienced in the art of pheasant transects. A real live biologist. He was all set to go and find the birds I was missing. To help him and to show me the errors of my counts, he had brought copies of survey records from years gone by. When I compared them to my surveys, I had to admit, the numbers I had recorded were … well, they were more than a little low. My surveys could be considered to be right off the scale. Maybe I don't know what I'm doing, I had to admit, but silently and to myself.

"Look, Bob, we know the numbers are down," he confided in me. "But, they're not down this much. You're pretty new to this line of work, aren't you?" he asked.

"Yeah, I guess so," I reluctantly admitted.

"There's some folks up north, thinking that you were missing the pheasants." Then as an afterthought he added. "I've heard it suggested that maybe you've been counting meadowlarks instead."

"You're kidding me," I mumbled. I had to admit that I'd never seen a Meadowlark before I arrived at Brooks, but that comment was an insult.

Later in the day, I was driving the green station wagon slowly along one of the transect roads in the Duchess area. I had stored the comment about the meadowlarks in a corner of my brain, for future use.

I had lots of time to think as I inched the car along and scanned the road for a sign of pheasant broods. It was my first meeting with a real live biologist and here I was, on a field trip, actually working with him. I was about to receive the benefit of how an expert ran a brood survey count. Shape up and enjoy it Bobby, I told myself. This is a real learning opportunity. Yeah, just thinking about it made me feel much better.

"There they are! STOP!" screamed my passenger, the expert, just as I hit the brakes, for I too had seen the elusive little bird. That little bird, a pheasant chick, was stretched out like a skinned squirrel. The little brown streak darted along the edge of the road then turned and raced into the grass. Just like that he was out of sight.

In his haste to point out the bird, my passenger obviously did not think I had seen it. He certainly was not anticipating my great reflexes and instant reaction to the bird. I almost put my foot through the floorboards when I slammed on the brakes.

"Oooooffff," groaned my partner, the wind was knocked out of him, as he slammed into the dash board. At the same time he jammed his fist into the windshield and let loose with a few choice words. But, he was one tough sucker and he recovered quickly.

"Stop the car and follow me," he roared excitedly as he threw open the door. The tires on the green station wagon had not skidded to a stop before his feet hit the road. He was not able to gain his balance and sprawled into the grass on the edge of the road.

"C'mon, man. I'll show you how this is done," he sang out as he scrambled to his feet.

"I'm with ya," I hollered back. When the wheels stopped skidding, I, too, bailed out of the green station wagon. I raced around the front and headed for the tall grass.

Through the waist high grass along the edge of the

road charged my passenger. "HEEAAAH," he screamed at the top of his lungs. He waved his arms, clapped his hands and raced around in the grass.

Suddenly, there was a fluttering of little wings, a meadowlark burst from the grass near the edge of the field and flew for its very life from the apparent madman.

"Meadowlark," I called out loud and clear as I raced for the grass.

"Meadowlark." I yelled louder just in case my passenger, the pro, missed my first call. It was important for him to know that I knew which bird had flown. Also the loud noise would insure that I got my share of scaring in.

Down into the ditch ran my passenger, screaming, waving, clapping and stomping. I too ran into the ditch.

"Fly. Fly. Fly you mothers, fly," I screamed. More fluttering of wings, from beneath my feet. "Pheasant. Hen." I sang out as the big bird burst from her hiding place and flapped out across the prairie.

"There's more," yelled my passenger. The sight of the hen seemed to be an added stimulant and he increased his efforts. He raced around in the grass, back and forth, from one edge of the ditch to the other, faster and faster he ran. Darting first one way, then the other, screaming and yelling at the top of his lungs. "There's more. C'mon, let's flush them out of here."

It was quite a sight, seeing a real pro at work. Then, suddenly, there was a lot of rustling in the grass. There was so much commotion, it looked like a whole flock of birds were ahead of him. Grass was being thrashed violently as the birds fled ahead of him.

"There's more. There's more right there. See them?" he yelled excitedly. His efforts reached new heights as he raced in a straight line toward the rapid movements and the rustling grass.

Then, out of the grass burst the biggest and the most scared old jack-rabbit that I have ever seen. Across the field bounced the bunny as fast as his legs would carry him.

"Jack-bunny," I called out, again loud and clear. "Jack-bunny."

Undeterred by the false alarm, my passenger raced back through the ditch and the tall grass. The excitement of spooking something out seemed to have renewed his energy. Around and around he raced. He flapped his arms. He screamed like a wild man.

I had laid claim to my own patch of grass and I, too, charged around wildly, still waving my arms, stomping my feet and shouting.

"Haaa," yelled my partner as he almost stepped on another bird. He had raced right past its hiding spot. But, he had spooked it, and up it flew, from the grass behind him, beating its little wings frantically.

"Pheasant. Chick." I called out once more. The little bird let out a couple of squawks as it flew away. "Pheasant chick. Probably a rooster," I added. I thought I'd let him know that I knew only the roosters squawked when they were flushed.

Like two idiots the two of us charged around through the grass for several more minutes. But there were no more birds, no more bunnies. Only two idiots, knee deep in the grass in the ditch.

Finally we stopped and stood there looking at each other on this fine summer day. I was quite pleased with myself, correctly identifying each bird and animal flushed.

Standing in the ditch it was peaceful and quiet. Except ... except for the sound of the motor. A motor was idling.

"Stupid. Stupid. Stupid," I cursed myself. If I had learned one thing during my time running transects, it was to pull the green station wagon over to the side of the road, turn the ruddy motor off, set the emergency brakes and close the ruddy door.

I turned to go back to the station wagon and tend to my neglected chores, lest I be chastised for that. But, I stopped in my tracks when I looked at the scene. The station wagon was stopped all right, right in the middle of the road, and both doors were wide open. But the motor was off. It was not my motor I heard, but another. My partner, the pro, and I had company.

The second motor belonged to the old fellow who was sitting in a beat up truck parked right behind the green station wagon.

"Oh, no," I moaned out loud as I looked at the old fellow. I gave the old guy a weak smile and a half hearted wave as I slunk back to the green station wagon. He ignored both.

"I was just getting a little help on my pheasant count ...," I started to explain. But stopped when I saw the old boy was not impressed.

He just sat there staring straight ahead. He knew, as

well as I, that he had just witnessed the dance of two idiots.

Sheepishly, I slid into the green station wagon and started the motor. As I inched the green station wagon over to the side of the road three words kept running through my head. Perception. Relationships. Image.

"You blew them all," I cursed. Then I thanked the division for having the foresight for not yet providing me with a uniform.

KEEP YOUR EYES PEELED
FOR A LONE DOE

"Keep your eyes peeled for a lone doe," my partner advised me as we drove slowly along the dirt road. I strained my eyes, scanning the prairie on the huge grazing leases south of Brooks. "At this time of the year the doe will be very close to her fawn," he continued. "She'll have just dropped the little guy and we'll have to look for him."

Thus began my initiation in the antelope fawn tagging program. We had left Brooks early in the morning and travelled south along the main road toward Lake Newell. Finding an access road, or fire guard, we turned left and headed east, out across the prairie, into the small hills and swales. We travelled very slowly over the gently rolling hills, searching for any sign of an antelope.

"There's one," whispered my partner as we crested a small rise. He pointed to a lone doe pronghorn antelope standing on a hillside about 200 yards ahead. She stood, rigid, like a statue, and watched. My partner brought the vehicle to a stop and shut off the motor. The little doe barked a couple of times, then turned her head, looking behind her. Slowly, she turned and trotted over the hill and out of sight. There was no panic, no wild dash for freedom. She acted like she was alone on this almost barren ground.

I eyeballed the prairie, out where the doe had been standing. There wasn't enough grass on the whole hillside to cover a dinner plate.

"Let's go. She's alone," I said to my partner. "There's no fawn here."

I expected him to start the vehicle and drive on looking for better prospects; instead, he grabbed his binoculars and stepped out.

"Did you see one get up and run with the doe?" he asked.

"Not unless it was a phantom," I chuckled. "She's probably a dry doe."

"Well, then, that little guy's got to be there somewhere," he said assuringly. "Now all we gotta do is find it."

My partner was very busy, carefully studying the hillside. I took another look as well. But no matter how hard I looked, that hillside looked about as bare as a baby's bottom. The grass, where there was grass, was no longer than a couple of day's growth of chin whiskers. The landscape was mostly dirt, bare ground, here and there a smattering of small, coloured rocks. To add to the flavour, the odd prickly pear cactus hugged the ground. I couldn't believe that it would provide any cover whatsoever, let alone hide an antelope fawn. I couldn't see any fawn.

"Sure," I replied sceptically. "And just how are we supposed to do that?"

"Well, the first thing you do is you take your binoculars and get out of the car. Then you come around here and I'll show you," came the tired response.

I took the glasses, the pair of old beat up 7 x 35 Bushnells that I had come to hate. I was not yet out of the car and already I could feel my right eye-ball being sucked out of its socket. Somehow, I had to get me a new or at least a better pair of binoculars.

"Okay, so now that we're out here standing on the prairie on a nice morning, what do we do next?" I asked.

"Let's see now," he said. "The doe was standing over in that direction, right?" he asked and pointed to the hill where we had first seen her. "You agree with that?"

"I can't argue with that," I chuckled.

"Now, the way I figure it, she's dropped her fawn and it'll be lying on the hill somewhere, probably within 50 to 100 yards from where she was standing. What do you think?" he asked.

I felt like an idiot as I stood there gazing at the barren hillside.

"I doubt it," I chuckled. "If there was a fawn on that

hill, we'd have seen it by now. Look at it; there's nothing there. There's no place for it to hide," I said as I once more cast a searching eye across the ground, just to make sure I hadn't missed something. It still looked the same, the odd stem of grass, here and there a small rock and a prickly pear cactus. The ground was almost bare.

"They're hard to see," replied my partner. "Those little guys blend right in with the scenery. You won't be able to see them with the naked eye. You need to use the binoculars to scan the hillside and hope that you can pick them out." He raised his glasses and very slowly started to glass the area around where the doe had been standing.

I watched my partner for a few seconds wondering if he was maybe just pulling my leg. Then, reluctantly, I lifted the binoculars and pointed them at the hillside close to the spot where the doe had been standing. Now the hillside was blurry and my eyes started to hurt. It would not be long before I had a splitting headache. I closed one eye, then tried to adjust the lens. Slowly I began to comb the surrounding area.

Through the haze and blur, I tried to pick out a small clump of grass. The blur made it look like the whole county was covered in grass. I tried to imagine a large brown blurry eye peering back at me. But try as I might, not one eye grew out from any of the grasses.

Maybe it was hiding behind one of the many small rocks, I thought. I began to search for small rocks looking for a small head to be peeking out from behind it. The rocks too, were blurry, but they were blurry in many different colours. The hues and swirls of colour were magnified through the binoculars, particularly the oranges, which seemed to stand out.

My eyes began to water, burn and hurt. Several minutes had passed, my eyes needed a change, a rest. I changed my method of operation and I had progressed from carefully screening a small section of the hill through one blurry lens to quickly sweeping the binoculars over its surface. Then, I swept them across the distant hills. Ah yes, it was much more soothing this way. My eyes stopped watering. The burning had ceased. The aches and pain in my eyes and head were easing. There was nothing to see on his barren countryside. I was enjoying the calm when my partner rudely interrupted. I had closed my eyes.

"I've got him," whispered my partner excitedly.

"Who," I asked. This sudden turn of events sort of caught me off guard. I opened my eyes and dropped the binoculars. I cast a quick glance at my partner. I half expected to see him splitting a gut laughing at me. But such was not the case. He was standing there, his binoculars trained on a piece of the prairie, a piece of the prairie that it appeared was very close to the spot where I had first seen the doe. I followed his direction and once more lifted my binoculars. This time, I only closed one eye as I scanned the area. Still nothing. I opened the other eye and looked through both lenses. Instantly the eye-sucking blur greeted me.

"Sorry," I said and dropped my glasses. "I can't see anything."

"Okay," he answered patiently. "Can you see where I'm looking?"

"Yeah. That's the same area that I looked at when I first started to glass the hill. I see lots of rocks and grass and dirt, but I don't see anything that looks like an antelope."

"Oh, yeah. Lookit 'im. He's lying right there among those small rocks about half way up the hill. He's a cute little guy and lookit 'im, he's looking straight at us. Can't you see 'im?" he warbled excitedly.

"No," I mumbled. "I can't see him."

"You just keep lookin' at that hillside. You can't miss him. He's starin' right at us," my partner stated happily.

I must have tried his patience to the nth degree as I alternately searched the hillside with bare eye and blurry binoculars.

"Let me try your binoculars," I finally asked. "I can't see nothing through these."

"Sure," he said and we exchanged glasses.

Once more, I looked at the hillside, this time with nice clear lenses. Lo and behold, I too finally spotted the little guy. It was hard to believe that on the bald headed prairie with nothing higher than three to four inches this little fellow had been lying in plain sight and watching us all the time. There he was with his little legs tucked under him and his head and neck stretched out in front of his body. He was facing us, looking us right in the eye, so to speak. Man, I thought, does he ever blend into the surroundings.

"You're right," I replied happily. "He certainly is a cute little fella."

"No wonder you couldn't see him," snorted my partner. "You haven't got your binoculars focused."

"Yeah," I replied. "I've been having some trouble with that."

"You better learn how to focus them if you're going to keep looking for antelope fawns."

"Right," I replied. "I'll work on that."

"Okay," said my partner as he handed me back my binoculars. "Back to work."

"Yeah, let's go get him," I answered ready for action.

"Whoa. Whoa. Not so fast. Let's just take a minute longer and search the area some more," said my partner. "It's not uncommon for does to have twins. We wouldn't want to miss one."

Now that I had an idea of what we were looking for and that I was not being the butt of some joke I began to search the hillside in earnest. I would leave no fuzzy, blurry stone unturned.

One fawn was all that my partner could find before he called an end to the search and laid out a plan to capture the little guy. In the back of his vehicle he had a large six-foot metal hoop that had mesh netting stretched loosely to it.

"This," explained my partner, "is what we use to catch the little critter."

"I thought that when they were lying down like that they were pretty tame and you could just walk up and pick them up," I said, more or less questioning the need for the net.

"Not hardly," chuckled my partner. "You get within a couple of feet of these little guys and they jump and run on you. He's probably only a day old, but believe me they can run like the wind," he said. "I'll use this and show you how it's done. Here. You take this piece of white rag and walk toward him. Wave the rag over your head and stop when you're about 25 feet from him. That'll keep his attention focused on you."

Holding the rag in my right hand over my head I began to wave it and slowly advanced towards the little antelope nestled tightly to the ground. As I got closer I began to see him a little more clearly, but if I hadn't known he was there I could easily have walked within a few feet and never seen him. He lay perfectly still with his eyes focused on me and now I could see the ears lying back, held flat against the head and neck. Not once did I see so much as a hair move.

While I stood and waved the flag, my partner circled around behind the antelope. He was crouched as low to the ground as he could get and held the hoop out in front of him. The leading part of the hoop was so low to the ground, I thought for sure it would scrape. Slowly, he approached while I continued to wave the surrender flag to the day-old antelope fawn.

When the leading edge of the hoop was about a foot away from the fawn, my partner leaped forward throwing the hoop up and over the startled fawn. The sudden movement spooked the little antelope, he bounded to his feet in an instant, but too late. The hoop came down around him and pinned him to the prairie soil. We rushed in to subdue it and prevent its struggling from causing any injury. Very carefully we extracted it from the mesh and I held it, just like a baby.

As soon as it was picked up, it stopped its struggling, but I could feel its little heart pounding.

The fawn was sexed, weighed and a number of measurements taken. Then came time for the identifying marking.

"There's no use doing this unless you're able to track the animal afterwards," explained my partner. The little antelope fawn was tagged with a metal ear tag that bore an identifying number. Attached to the metal tag would be seismic flagging of various colour combinations. The numbers and colours would be recorded with each animal's vital statistics.

"We'll come back later on when the fawns and does have joined the herds and see how many have survived," said my partner. "Then, this winter, when the division conducts the antelope surveys, they'll be able to identify these fawns by their ear tags and flagging. This will give us a good idea of the survival rate for fawns."

My partner was right about that little antelope being able to run. When I released the little guy he took off like a scalded rat, the coloured flagging trailing from his ear. He looked like an escapee from the circus as he bolted for freedom and quickly disappeared from view over the top of the hill. I ran to the top to see if I could see him again, but he was nowhere in sight. Probably lying right in front of me, I thought, as I looked out across the bald headed prairie.

As soon as we had put everything back in the car again, we were off looking for another doe and more fawns. Not all of the fawns were as cooperative as that first one. We spotted several more and each time were able to approach within a few feet. But several of them jumped and ran before the hoop could be thrown over them. Once on their feet, there was absolutely no way that they were going to be caught as they sped to freedom. By the end of the day, we had captured four or five and would return the next day for more.

It didn't take us long the next morning before we had spotted the first fawn. By now I had the not too blurry left lens of the binoculars working pretty well and was considerably more help to my partner in searching them out. I knew what to look for but, more importantly, I now believed in the process.

We had tagged a number of antelope fawns and, although we kept moving, looking for new animals each day, we did pass through much of the same country. I thought it strange that we did not see any of those we had previously tagged. One afternoon we were driving through the area where we had tagged the majority of the fawns. We saw many does, many does with fawns, but no fawns with ear tags with brightly coloured flagging.

"There's one," my partner finally shouted happily. Sure enough, off in the distance, close to a clump of sagebrush, we spotted a length of seismic flashing. It was easy to see as it fluttered in the breeze. I could see it, even without my one-eyed binoculars. It was a fawn we had tagged only a couple of days earlier. We could see the flagging but not the little fellow, so we decided to take a closer look. We did not want to disturb the youngster too much so we parked the vehicle back from the brush and slowly approached. My partner was taking notes and identifying which fawn it was by the colour combinations.

The fawn lay so still and quiet, we were able to get right up to it. But, there was no fawn. There were only the remains of the little fawn. He had been killed and eaten by coyotes. All that remained was part of the head and the ear containing the tag.

"Well, look at it this way," I said to a very dejected partner. "The program isn't a complete failure. At least you've got one return."

That, he concluded without much thought, was a very uncalled for remark. But as the week passed and the miles rolled by we failed to locate any fawns with ear tags.

The next fawn we captured was tagged and then we followed it after it was released. It ran for quite a distance before it resumed its natural instinct to lie down, be still and blend into the surrounding country side. Although he lay perfectly still, the strips of colourful seismic flagging were very evident as they flapped on the gentle prairie breeze. This little fellow, lying so still, now carried with him the kiss of death.

RATTLER IN A JUG

"Did you see that snake?" asked the waitress at the Country Kitchen in Brooks.

"Which one?" I chuckled. As was the custom, I along with a number of others had just sat down at a table to enjoy a coffee and a little camaraderie. I figured her reference to the snake referred to one of the regulars who had already arrived. I looked around the room to see who she could be referring to. There were a number of likely candidates.

"Which one of these snakes bit you this morning?" someone else laughed.

"I mean a snake," she said disgustedly. "A snake. A real live snake."

"Well, that describes a number of these dudes all right," I replied and waved my arm around the room. We all had a good belly laugh.

"It was a snake. A rattlesnake," she replied. This time she showed a little bit of excitement.

"Where," I asked. Now I was interested. What was a rattlesnake doing in the Country Kitchen? Suddenly, I wasn't nearly as cocky as I had been. If there was a rattlesnake in here, this was a job for me and I wasn't really that sure I wanted it.

"Oh, it's gone now," she said.

"Where'd it go?" I asked.

"This guy came in here this morning for breakfast and he had it in a jug. Didn't you see it? It just about made me sick," she said and faked putting her fingers down her throat.

"No, I didn't see it, but I'd like too. Any idea where it is now?"

"How would I know?" she replied. "It was the creepiest thing. This rancher just came in here and set the thing on the table. Then he had breakfast and left."

"Did he say where he was going?"

"Nope. Just paid his bill and left. Took the snake with him, too."

I didn't figure that a snake in a jug, especially a rattlesnake, would be that hard to find in Brooks. I skipped coffee and left the café. I turned south, walking slowly. I checked every shop on the street. The main purpose of my search was to have a good close-up look at a rattlesnake. In the jug, of course. I had heard many stories and tales of rattlers along the Red Deer, Bow and South Saskatchewan rivers. Most, of course, were meant to scare me and I had to admit that I had often trod pretty softly along the banks of the rivers. However, I had yet to see one in the wild or, for that matter, in a jug.

Through an open door, I could see a group of men gathered at the back of the barber shop. That looked like as good a place as any to begin the search. The folks gathered at the back of the shop were pretty excited. I, too, could feel the excitement building as I approached the group. I wanted to see that snake, and I was sure hoping that it was still in the jug. I cautiously looked over a shoulder, and there it was, a real live honest to goodness prairie rattlesnake, coiled up at the bottom of a one-gallon jug. The same type that we used to buy cheap wine in. Ah, the good ol' days when cheap wine was all we could afford.

Had I not been so excited about seeing the rattler, I would have been disappointed by the size of it. I had expected something like the rattlers that cowboys always shot in the movies. A snake six feet long, the size of my wrist. This little guy was only about two feet long and about as big around as a cigar. But, on this occasion, he was big enough to be the most exciting thing that had happened in Brooks for some time.

The rattler and the rancher were very popular. Each person in the group was wanting to borrow the jug with the snake just to take and show to someone else, of course. But the rancher who had brought the snake to town was having nothing to do with lending out his trophy.

"No. No," he responded to each request. "I figure that would be the quickest way to lose him."

"What are you gonna do with 'im?" someone asked.

"I'm gonna take him back to the ranch and release him where I caught him."

One man was persistent. He had a plan and all he needed was a little cooperation. He finally convinced the rancher that if he lent him the snake he would put it in a place where he could show his wife and the rancher could keep an eye on it right from the comfort of the barber shop, even in the chair, while getting his hair cut, if he chose. Now the rancher was not an unreasonable man and he allowed himself to be convinced that indeed the man's plan could work, whereupon he surrendered the jug. The ecstatic man, with jug in hand, with rattlesnake in jug, walked to the front of the barbershop followed closely by the rancher and the rest of the crowd.

Out the front door he strode, just like he owned the world, straight to a car parallel parked on the street within a few feet of the barbershop. Opening the passenger's door, he very carefully positioned the jug on the front seat. Then after closing the door, he turned and winked to the group crowding the window of the barber shop then strutted off down the street. There was no doubt. He was true to his word. The rancher could watch his prize while the man set his plan to work.

There was very little work accomplished by any in the crowd. The delay was lengthy but it did not deter any of the gallery. They all watched and eagerly waited. This was one event that no one was going to miss.

Finally, the man was spotted coming down the street and the crowd pressed closer to the window. He was not alone. When he arrived at the side of the car, his wife was with him. Being ever the gentleman that he was, he stepped briskly ahead and opened the door. He waited patiently for her to settle in and get comfortable and then gently closed the door. Not once during this whole time did he look down or inside the car. He was taking no chances on tipping his hand and spoiling the surprise.

With his wife comfortably settled, he casually walked around the back of the car and turned his head to glance at the barbershop. He was not disappointed, the gang was there with their noses pressed against the glass, for this was the big moment and not one to be missed. He gave the boys a knowing wink and a big old smile as he calmly strutted to the driver's door and reached for the handle.

So casual and confident was he that he did not steal even one little peek at that jug. It had to be close to his wife. It was probably touching her. No, Joe Cool himself, looked out across the street as he opened his door and deliberately backed his butt into the car. Casually he swung around and brought his feet in and under the steering wheel. Both hands were on the steering wheel and he looked straight ahead, pausing for a few seconds before turning to his wife. From inside the barbershop we could all see his lips moving as he spoke to his wife. She turned and glared at him. But, we had to hand it to him, he was one cool customer. He turned and looked straight ahead at some object down the street.

It seemed that some heated discussion was transpiring between the two. The little lady was not too pleased. Could it have been that her shopping had been cut short at his insistence? Finally, he pried his eyes away from the street and turned to face his wife. There was a sly, devilish grin on his face as he spoke, then he looked down.

Up to this point, the boys in the barbershop had been holding their breath. They didn't need to read lips for what happened next. The man's eyes bulged and the veins on his neck looked about to burst. He couldn't believe what he was seeing.

"GET THE HELL OUT OF THE CAR!" he screamed. The door on the driver's side burst open as he bailed out. He sprawled onto the street in his haste. Just as quickly, he bounced to his feet and raced around to the passenger's side.

"GET OUT OF THE CAR. GET OUT OF THE CAR," he wailed.

In the barber shop, the boys howled with laughter. It was a show beyond their expectations.

Now, the little lady, who had not appeared to be to happy at the prospect of having to get into the car in the first place, was even less enthusiastic about being told to get out, let alone being yelled at. She sat firm while her husband, the jokester, raced around the car screaming and yelling.

"GET OUT, I TOLD YOU," he bellowed once more as he reached the door.

Without a second's hesitation, he yanked the door open and grabbed his wife by the arm and shoulder. With a mighty heave, he dragged her unceremoniously from the car and dropped her to the sidewalk. She lay there sprawled out on the sidewalk with her feet still in the car. Upon seeing this, the frazzled man then grabbed an arm and dragged her across the cement until her entire body was clear, out of harm's way.

The boys in the barbershop whooped and hollered as they streamed out the door for a better look. Well, if one thought that the little lady had been unhappy when she returned to the car, that was nothing compared to the mood she was in now. Slowly and with as much dignity as she had left, the lady lifted herself off the sidewalk, she turned and faced the man, her husband, the prankster.

"Snake," he muttered. "It was a snake." The poor fellow was no longer Joe Cool. He had been reduced to a scared shaking specimen as he stood before his wife and tried to explain his actions.

She glared at him for several long seconds, then turned and stomped away. She found very little amusement in her husband's actions and absolutely no humour at all in the laughing, howling troop that had gathered on the sidewalk.

As his wife stormed away, the man returned his attention to his car. He looked, very cautiously, through the open door. He was careful not to get too close.

"Look," he sputtered to the crowd and pointed to the front seat. "Just … just lookit that."

Looking into the front seat of the car, I could immediately see the cause for his concern. For there on the seat was the jug exactly where he had placed it right between where the passenger and driver would sit. Lying on the seat, smack dab under the lip of the jug, was the lid. The jug, however, was empty. The empty jug spoke volumes. The harmless little joke he was going to spring on his wife had backfired. It certainly explained his actions. Why he panicked and even worse, why he had thrown his poor wife around getting her out of the car. Somewhere in the interior of his car there was a rattlesnake, coiled and ready to strike. Now, not even he was safe in the car.

"I … I could have been bit. My wife could have been bit. We both could have been killed," he mumbled, his voice cracking.

The boys from the barber shop hung on his every word. "Har, har, har," they howled each time he spoke.

"I tell you, it's not funny boys. This is not funny at all," he said seriously. "My wife could have been killed." Then, he got down on his hands and knees and he tried to get a look under the front seats. From a safe distance of course.

"Go on," someone urged. "Stick your nose in there. You're not gonna see a snake from that distance. Not if it's curled up on the springs."

"Har, har, har," came another course of laughter.

"C'mon, don't be such a coward," someone howled. "Put your hand under the seat. If there's a snake in there, he'll grab it."

But the poor man saw absolutely no humour in his situation. There was a rattlesnake loose in his car and he knew it. And he had absolutely no idea how he was going to get it out. He was no longer in a jovial mood. This was serious business.

"I may never be able to use this car again," he

mumbled as he peered into the vacant car. The more he fussed and fretted the more the boys howled.

Very carefully and from a distance, the man searched his car as thoroughly as he could. As thoroughly as he could without actually touching it, that is. But there was no sign of the snake. Except for the odd little hiss and jangle from the boys on the sidewalk, there was not even a hint of a rattle from anywhere inside the car. This was not a good time in the man's life.

Meanwhile, as he crawled around outside his car, trying to get a good look under the seats, another scene was unfolding. Out behind the barbershop, a puddle of red liquid that smelled suspiciously like cheap sweet wine was slowly seeping into the ground. And, somewhere north of Brooks on a gravel road, the rancher was on his way home, back to the Red Deer River valley. Sitting on the front seat with him, with the lid screwed down tight was the real gallon jug. Resting in a tight coil and watching his every move was a little rattlesnake, the little rattlesnake. Soon the lid would be removed and the little snake set free.

DEER FOR THE OLD FOLKS

"Yoo-hoo, Mr. Adams. Officer. Officer Adams," the lady called. The sound of the urgent voice chased me down the main drag in Brooks.

I spun on my heel to see who it was. By the tone of the voice it was someone in need of assistance. The lady was running down the street after me. In one hand she was carrying a heavy bag. In the other, a purse which she was waving above her head. Yes, she was in a hurry and obviously in need of my help. I hurried back to meet her.

"Yes, can I help you?" I asked.

"Oh, I hope so," she replied. She was all out of breath from the run and stood there gasping.

"I hope so too," I replied. "Tell me. What's the problem? What can I do?"

"Mr. Adams," she panted, still out of breath. "You … you wouldn't happen to have any more of that deer meat would you?"

"Deer meat!" I replied. I was at a loss. "What deer meat are you talking about?"

"You know, deer meat," she panted. "Deer meat, like the deer meat you gave us last fall."

I took a second look at the lady, then I recognized her. Sure, I thought, now I know who she is. She was one of the ladies who worked at the Old Folks Home, whom I had met the previous fall.

During my first hunting season on the prairies, I had seized several big game animals. There were deer, antelope and also several hundred whitefish and jackfish.

Before the hunting season was over, the butcher at the IGA was on my case.

"Bob," he would say every time I walked past his meat counter, or brought in another animal. "My freezer's full of the queen's beef. I've got no room for my own meat any more. You got to get some of it out of here."

"I will," I promised. "I will. Just as soon as the hunting season is over, I'll get it out."

"Look, Bob," he said one day and he was very serious. "Today, Bob. You get that meat out of here by closing time today, or I'll throw it in the garbage."

"Tomorrow," I replied. "Please just give me until tomorrow. I'll be around first thing in the morning and pick it up."

"You've got until tomorrow," he sighed. "But,

remember, if you're not here first thing in the morning, it goes into the garbage."

I raced back to the office and quickly phoned the Powers-that-be.

"What can I do?" I asked once I had explained my predicament.

"Why don't you ask your boss?"came the helpful reply.

"Because he's in the field. I have no idea where he is."

"Well, then, give it to the needy," said the Powers-that-be. "You can't just go and give confiscated meat to any Tom, Dick and Harry. You gotta give it to the needy people in the community."

"Needy," I repeated. "But, other than me, I don't know any needy people here. I'm probably the most needy person in town," I replied.

"What about welfare," he said. "Don't you know anybody on welfare?"

"No, I don't know anybody on welfare, either," I said. "How about the hospital, could I give it to the hospital?"

"No. No," he snorted. "You can't give it to the hospital, but I do know who you can give it to."

"Who's that?" I asked quickly.

"The old folks," he replied. "Give it to the old folks."

"But, I don't know any old folks around here either," I informed him. He seemed to be forgetting that I had been in Brooks for less than a month.

"Mr. Adams," he sighed. "Why don't you try the old folks home?" his voice sounded like he had gone the distance with a wayward child."

"What old folks home?" I asked.

"Isn't there an old folks home in Brooks?"

"I guess," I replied.

"You know, Adams, most of those old folks in this country were raised on wild meat," he informed me. "I'd just be willing to bet they'd appreciate the taste of a good venison steak now and again."

"I'd think that money's a bit tight with those old people, too," I added.

"That's right," he replied. "But remember, Adams, you have to hold all exhibits until the court case has been heard. You can only get rid of those animals that have been confiscated by the court."

"I'll try to remember," I replied.

"And Adams," he continued. "The queen's beef only goes to the needy. I don't want to hear of you sharing it with your friends."

His suggestion was the solution, I decided, because it didn't take long to confirm that there was seniors' home in Brooks. Now, if I could get rid of all the meat at one place, it would take a load off my mind. And a load out of the IGA butcher shop.

I had lots of help the next morning. The butcher and his staff loaded deer meat that had been confiscated until the back of my green station wagon was once more loaded to the roof.

With hat in hand, and several hundred pounds of venison in the back of the green station wagon, I drove over to the old folks home. And walked into the kitchen.

"Can I help you?" asked the lady who met me at the door to the kitchen. She looked me up and down suspiciously.

"I hope so," I said. "I've got some of the queen's beef in the station wagon, and I was wondering if the old folks might like a feed of deer meat."

"Deer meat … oow boy. Oow, I don't know about deer meat," she replied hesitantly. "Deer is always so messy and stinky."

"Not this deer meat. I can assure you it's in real good shape," I quickly added.

"Where did you get it," she asked.

"I'm a fish and wildlife officer," I informed her. "And the meat has been confiscated to the Crown."

"Oh, I don't know. Wild meat is always so much work to prepare," she replied. "There's always so much hair in it. I just shudder at the thought of all the work it takes to prepare it. And I hate picking a piece of hair out before I eat it."

"You don't have to worry about hair this time," I replied. "This meat is in real good shape. The butcher over at the IGA prepared it, and he's real fussy."

"I skinned a lot of the animals myself, and the butcher and I, we cleaned the meat up real good."

"Well, I suppose I can have a look at them," she said, but it was obvious that she was reluctant to have the likes of wild meat in her kitchen. "We get lots of hunters who come around and offer us wild meat," she said as we walked out to my car. "Most of the time, it's because their wives won't cook it and they want some place to dump it."

"Well, I'm not a hunter, and like I said, this is confiscated meat and it's been well cared for."

"Oh, I know. I know," she replied. "Everyone tells me the same thing."

"Well, I can assure you, this is deer for the old folks," I chuckled. I was hoping to soften her up a bit, because I wasn't sure what I would do with all the meat if she refused to take it. I really had no place to store the meat for an extended period of time and there did not appear to be a better place then the old folks home.

"I've got it right here in the back of the station wagon," I informed her and opened the back door for her to see.

"Oh, my goodness," she gasped. It was obvious that this was no ordinary run of the mill load of dear meat. This was the mother load and it was all hers for the taking. "I ... I had no idea. Well, yes ... yes, certainly. I'd love to help you out. How much can I have?" she asked.

"How much do you want?"

"All of it. I'll take it all," she replied hastily. She was pretty excited when she looked at the meat.

"Good. Good. Oh yeah, that's real good," I sighed, relieved that I had found a bona fide place that would take the meat and sign the exhibit forms.

"You know, for a minute there, I thought you just wanted to dump a bunch of carcasses on my door step. I had no idea that they were all cut up and they're even wrapped."

She stood there beaming at the boxes stacked in the back of the green station wagon. Each box was heaped with packages of meat all wrapped in brown butcher's paper and marked in bold black letters with its own identifier. HAMBURGER. CHOPS. STEW. STEAK. ROAST.

"You'd be surprised at some of the garbage that people try to drop off here. We have to be so careful," she informed me.

"Okay then. You just tell me where you want it and I'll carry it in," I said. I wanted to get rid of it before she changed her mind. Just the thought of getting rid of the meat was a big relief. I felt like jumping into the air and clicking my heels together.

"No. No," she chuckled. "You've already done enough. You come on in and sit down. You rest and have a cup of coffee. I'll call some of the staff to do this."

"No, thanks," I objected to the offer. "I don't mind. I'll bring the boxes in and then you can do what you want with them." But there was no arguing with her. This was one determined happy lady and she would not take no for an answer. Before the first box was unloaded, I was sitting in the kitchen, enjoying a cup of coffee. Several staff members, all ladies, were busy carting the packages of meat out of the station wagon and bringing them into the kitchen area.

I had to admit that it was a pretty good feeling. Not only because I had got rid of the meat, but because I was helping. My little gesture was making a difference.

As I sipped the coffee, I could see vivid pictures of the old folks. These were people who had spent their life on the prairie, surviving the great depression, the dirty thirties. Most of them probably depended on wild meat to survive. Oh, yes, I could just see the joy in their eyes when they tied into a good feed of venison. I could even see the smiles of happiness on their faces at the very thought of a venison roast.

I took another sip of coffee and smiled. Man, but it felt good to be able to help the old folks.

Yes, the very thought of giving these folks a small glimpse back to younger days gave me a very good feeling. This was one cup of coffee that I could honestly say I was enjoying.

Over the next several months, I delivered more venison and I was also able to provide enough fresh whitefish for several meals. Oh, but the old folks were going to live high on the hog.

Now, one of the ladies who had helped unload my green station wagon on that first day was standing in front of me, all out of breath from running. And at that time, I had no more deer for the old folks.

"I'm sorry," I replied sadly. "But we don't have any meat right at this time."

"But, we're all out of wild meat now," she informed me.

I felt the sadness in her eyes, for I too would have loved to be able to provide the old folks with another good feed of venison. But, the summer season was not really a good time of the year to be looking for wild meat. There had not been a single seizure of an illegal animal for months and that meant there were no confiscations to disperse.

"I am truly sorry," I repeated. "But I just don't have any more at this time. I'm fresh out. But, hunting season is just around the corner. Then if things go like they did last year, I should be able to stock up your larder again."

"I know," she smiled. "We all appreciate so much what you're doing. Please keep us in mind again."

"Oh, don't you worry now. I will," I assured her. "You know that you're number one on my list." Once again, I got that good feeling, just knowing that the old folks appreciated the wild meat.

"Oh, I'm so glad to hear that," she replied.

As we were standing there talking, I had an idea. Maybe the old folks were partial to one cut over the others.

"Tell me," I asked. "Is there one cut that is more popular with the old folks then the other?"

"With the seniors ... I don't know. Why?" she asked.

"Well, I was just thinking that if the old folks preferred one cut, say hamburger or steaks over roasts and chops, I could have the butcher cut the meat the way they like it."

"Oh, no. No. The meat's not for the seniors," she replied. "We can't serve any of that meat to the seniors."

"You can't," I blurted out.

"No. No," she chuckled. "We can't feed wild meat to the seniors. They're on very strict diets. Wild meat would just upset them and probably give them the runs. We never feed wild meat to the seniors."

"Well, what do you do with it then?" I asked.

"Oh, don't worry. It doesn't go to waste," she assured me. "We take it home, the staff, we take it home and eat it. It's very good."

"You mean, I took all that meat and fish over there and none of it went to feed the old folks."

"Oh no," she laughed again. "We can't feed wild meat to the seniors."

"You're kidding me, right?" I asked and chuckled. It was a sickly chuckle. "Please, tell me you're kidding."

"Oh, no. I'm not kidding. I'm quite serious," she replied.

"Yeah. I can see that, now."

"You will remember us when you get more meat, won't you?" she asked again.

"Sure," I replied. "I'll remember you. You can count on it. I'll remember you." At that point I was also remembering the strict instructions I had received from the Powers-that-be.

"Remember, Adams. The queen's beef goes to the needy,"

Once again, I was in need of the needy.

THIS IS HOW WE DO IT
IN THE NORTH

"WHOA. STOP. STOP," I screamed at the top of my lungs. I was flapping my arms up and down like a chicken with its head cut off. I was running as fast as I could as I chased the rapidly departing car across the ice.

"STOP, YOU IDIOT. YOU'VE SNAGGED THE DRAW-LINE," I screamed again.

My introduction to the commercial fishing industry in Alberta, southern Alberta to be exact, had certainly been a memorable one. One that I could honestly say I enjoyed immensely. In fact, I enjoyed it to such an extent that I started to look upon the lake as my lake.

I was eagerly looking forward to my second season with great anticipation. Then, I found out that I was going away. The division had decided to send me to school. After two hunting seasons and several commercial fisheries, I was going to get some training on how to be a game warden and that was good. However, it meant that I was going to miss most of the commercial fishery on Lake Newell and that was bad.

"Who's going to look after the commercial fishery on my lake?" I asked as soon as I learned of my fate.

"Don't worry about the lake, lad," I was advised. "We've run commercial fisheries long before you got here and we'll run commercial fisheries long after you're gone. We're gonna send someone down to work the lake while you're away. The only thing we want you to do is show him around when he gets there. Do you think you can handle that?"

"Yeah, I can handle that," I replied.

Then the moccasin telegraph began to vibrate. The moccasin telegraph was the unofficial voice of the division and had an excellent track record, being about 99 per cent accurate. Pending decisions spread swiftly from district to district and would proceed any official word by several days. The moccasin telegraph was fast; news seemed to travel along at about the speed of light.

The division was sending a retired fishery officer from northern Alberta, down to look after the fishery on Lake Newell. He's a crusty old fella. A no nonsense guy. A man of few words, said the moccasin telegraph.

The no nonsense part certainly caught my attention. Immediately, I started to wonder how had I stacked up during the past year. I figured that I, too, could be considered a no nonsense kinda guy.

During the past fisheries, I had picked up quite a few illegal nets and I had laid several charges. I had to chuckle when I thought about one of the fishermen I had charged with using a small-mesh net. He was not around when I arrived to check his gang of nets, and when I checked them I found one to be too small. I seized his net and his catch, then I returned to Brooks where I preserved and stored the evidence. It was a very unhappy fisherman who went to the RCMP to report his nets stolen. But I was a stickler for detail and that detail paid off. My actions proved to be faultless and the fisherman went before the courts and paid a fine for fishing with a small-mesh net.

I went through a lot of pain and effort to secure and preserve the evidence whenever I found an infraction. I smiled when I thought of the image I must have cast when checking small-mesh nets. There I was hunched over a net hole like a vulture hovering over a road kill. Down on my haunches I squatted, right at the edge of the hole where the net was being pulled through. About every 10 yards, I would take measurements. Perched at the edge of the hole with my nose right down to the water, I would measure 10 sometimes 20 different little diamond meshes. Man, I wondered, how many of those fishermen would have loved to walk over and give me a boot on the tail bone.

I made sure each net was properly dried and hung, then stored for presentation in court. Seized fish were alway kept frozen so they could be presented in court. I had not lost a single case and I was quite proud of my record. Yes, the care and diligence which I put into each case and how particular I had been whenever I seized a net had paid off. I figured that I too could be classified as a no nonsense kind of guy. I wondered if my technique would stand up to the scrutiny of an experienced no nonsense guy.

The day before the season began, the crusty old fella, the no nonsense guy, the man of few words from the north, arrived at the office. He walked in and stood at the counter. Slowly, he eyed the place.

"Hi, I'm Adams," I said. I extended my hand as I hastened from my office to greet him. He didn't waste many words or much time sizing me up. I figured I rated no more then a five-second glance. But I had a pretty good look at him.

The no nonsense guy who was going to be looking after my lake while I was gone was a wiry, well-kept fellow. He looked to be in pretty good shape for an old geezer on the long side of 60. He had a full head of snow-white hair and clean-shaven face. He looked like a man who had spent many hours, days and years on the water and ice. His face had a dark, wind-burned, leathery look. His hands were rough, chapped, with bulging knuckles, from the wear and tear of working fishing gear in freezing water. His fingers were gnarled, one finger permanently bent. Those hands had spent countless hours pulling nets in the worst of conditions. Yeah, I thought. This is my kinda guy, a no nonsense fish cop.

I was pretty eager to take this old vet out and show him what I knew.

"I'm Adams," I introduced myself again. "You're just in time. I'm just on my way out to the lake. I thought I'd take a look around and make sure no one's slippin' one in a little early."

He stared a hole right through me for a few seconds before responding.

"That's a good idea," he replied.

I felt pretty good that he agreed with my strategy. After all, we couldn't have anyone jumping the gun. But, from the look in his eye, I sort of got this feeling that he resented the fact that I had spoken without getting permission.

"I thought maybe you would like to join me," I added cautiously. "I can show you the lake and the preferred locations." I had learned last year that there were several areas that were more preferred than others. Large portions of the lake never saw a net. This I thought would be good information for anyone, even for a no nonsense guy.

"No," he replied.

"No. But . . . but, I thought you were here to take over when I left ...," I started to protest.

The cold stare he gave me was enough. I didn't need someone to draw me a picture. If I was going to go to the lake to make sure someone "didn't slip one in a little early," I was going by myself.

The no nonsense guy did not accompany me the next day either, the opening day of the fishery. Everywhere I looked there was a vehicle. Around each vehicle were three, four, five, six bodies. Holes were being dug. Nets were being stretched out on the ice. Jiggers were being pulled, their progress being followed by their scratching and clicking on the under ice surface. Nets were being drawn into the water. Stakes were being driven into the ice to mark each hole. Fish buyers were busy setting up their fish shacks, making boxes and gutting tables. The lake was a beehive of activity. I made a note of every activity. Tomorrow, with any luck, I'd be able to show the no nonsense guy every fisherman, every net and every fish buyer.

I raced around the lake, alone, renewing many old acquaintances. I recognized every face from the year before. Some I remembered better then others. Some knew me better then others. Some had wished they had never seen me.

"So young feller, I see you're back for another year," was the most common greeting I received.

"Only for a couple of days," I replied. "They're sending me on a course and they're bringing in a no nonsense guy from the north to look after you guys."

"That's the only thing that's consistent about you guys," one old fisherman stated.

"What's that?" I asked.

"Just about the time we get to know you; they move you out. Then they bring in some new guy that we gotta train all over again."

"Hey, that's a good one," I laughed.

"That's the truth son, you can count on it," he said shaking his head. "Just like death and taxes."

However, not all the greetings were as friendly.

"Nobody shot you yet?" snarled a very familiar face as I stepped from the car at another group of fishermen.

"Not yet," I replied.

"Well, someone will. You mark my words, you keep stickin' your nose into other people's business around here and someone's gonna shoot you. You can go to the bank on that," he replied.

"You still slipping in some tight gear?" I asked, being careful not to grin. It was the same fisherman who had gone to the RCMP and reported his nets stolen last year.

"You just mind yourself," he snarled. "If I was you, I'd be mighty careful. I'd be watching my step around here this year," he stated and picked up a needle bar, he smiled at me and drove it into the ice.

"Dig here," he said to one of the others. "We'll run the next net from here."

The next day, my last day, I went into the office before heading out to the lake. There he was, leaning on the counter, the no nonsense guy, all ready to go to work.

My cheerful "All ready to go to work?" was greeted with his usual response: a stare. However, when I left the office with my brief case and clip board, the no nonsense guy followed me out and down the stairs.

"We can take my car," I offered as we stepped out onto the sidewalk. He ignored me and walked over to his car. I got into the green station wagon and started it up. I thought the no-nonsense guy was just going to his car to get his brief case so I sat and waited for him.

I couldn't believe my eyes when I looked over my shoulder to see what was keeping him so long. He had backed his car away from the curb and was proceeding to drive away. I quickly shut off the motor, I grabbed my brief case and clip board and bailed out of the green station wagon. I waved at him as he drove by, but he didn't seem to notice. I was standing on the street with egg all over my face when he stopped, about 10 car lengths down the street. He stopped, but he didn't back up.

How stupid of me I thought when I had settled into the passenger seat of his nice new car. I should have known the no-nonsense guy would never lower himself to ride in a beater like the old green station wagon.

It was a long quiet trip to Lake Newell. When we arrived at the road leading to the north end of the lake, I pointed it out.

"We can get on the north end of the lake here," I mentioned. I pointed out a trail that angled over to the headgates on the north end of Lake Newell.

The no nonsense guy looked straight ahead and continued to drive. He drove south before finally taking the Kinbrook Island turn-off. As we neared the lake, I pointed out to a fish buyer's shack and a number of half-ton trucks parked around it. We drove right past the shack, past the half-ton trucks and out onto the lake. It didn't take a brain surgeon to realize that I was the one along for the ride. I wasn't sure what my role was, or if I had one. Best just to sit back and keep my mouth shut, I thought.

Sometimes we stopped near a group of fishermen. Then the no nonsense guy would talk, check the licenses, check the fish, measure the net and record the data. I would roll down the window and listen, but I'd stay in the car. Sometimes he would stop at a net site that had not yet been visited by the fishermen. Out on the ice, with not another soul around, except for myself that is, the no nonsense guy would get out of his car, take a needle bar out of the trunk and chip open the hole. Then he'd pull the net up, into the hole, and measure a few meshes. I'd stay in the car. The no nonsense guy, certainly, was a man of few words. When people were present, he spoke only those words that were necessary. He said absolutely nothing to me. I didn't exist.

We had experienced a lot of undersized gear last year. Many of these illegal nets were a good quarter of an inch under and it was just a matter of time before the no nonsense guy found one. Out, on a lonely stretch of lake, with not another soul around, he stopped at a gang of nets that had not yet been pulled. I recognized the stakes, the numbers and the location. The nets belonged to a fisherman I knew only too well. The man who only yesterday had asked me the question.

"Nobody shot you yet?" This man owned these nets.

"Hmm," grunted the no nonsense guy. He was holding a handful of twine in his hand and staring into the hole.

"C'mere and look at this," he snorted. "See here. This net is too small, see that?"

I got out of the car and walked over to the hole in the ice to look at the mesh he was measuring. For my benefit, he slid his metal tape into one of the mesh and snugged it up. I leaned over for a good close look.

"Right," I agreed. "It's too small."

"You get on down to the other end and cut it," he instructed me.

Maybe this was the break I needed, I thought, now that we had found an illegal net and he actually had something to show me. I hustled my butt the hundred yards down to the far end of the net. I chipped out the hole and lifted the drop line. I carefully pulled the cord and untied the illegal net. I was just ready to drop the loose end when it shot out of my hand. I thanked my lucky stars that I had leather mitts. I shook my hand and stared after the rope. It sang as it burned a groove in the ice. I couldn't believe how quickly it snaked over the ice and through the hole before disappearing into the water. Man, I thought, was that net ever strung tight. If I would have had that line wrapped around my hand, I could have lost a finger, maybe even my hand.

I stood up and took one more look down the hole. I shook my head then I turned to walk back to the car. It was impossible to believe, but once more the no nonsense guy was driving away from me.

"Hey," I called out. "You're leaving something behind, you … " but I stopped short when what appeared to be a rocket caught my eye. A rocket, which resembled a white fish suddenly shot out of the hole and went about fifty feet, straight up into the air it flew. It sailed high and far, in a graceful arc, before plummeting to the ice. The tail flipped a couple of times, then it lay there.

I couldn't believe what I had just seen. How, had that whitefish shot out of a hole in the ice like that? Meanwhile, the no-nonsense guy's car was getting farther and farther away. Then, another whitefish rocketed out of the hole, followed closely by another then another.

"WHOA. STOP. STOP," I screamed at the top of my

lungs. I was flapping my arms up and down like a chicken with its head cut off. I was running as fast as I could as I chased the rapidly departing car across the ice.

"STOP, YOU IDIOT. YOU'VE SNAGGED THE DRAW-LINE."

It didn't take long to figure out what had happened. The no-nonsense guy had taken his end of the net and tied it to the trailer hitch on his car. Then he placed the float line on one side of the mound of ice by the hole and the lead line on the other. As soon as I had released the net he drove off. The mound of ice had stripped the mesh and launched the fish into the air.

I looked over to where the no nonsense guy was driving his car. The car had slowed down and was making a big lazy circle back to the disaster. The float line and the lead line trailed behind. They were dancing along and whipping around like a couple of snakes behind his car. I examined the lines when he stopped and except for some loose cotton threads, there was not a single mesh left between them.

"What are you doing?" I asked. I couldn't believe my eyes. After all the care I had taken with handling gear, small mesh or otherwise, I couldn't believe what lay before me.

"Pulling an illegal net, " he replied quite happily. It was the first time that I had seen the no nonsense guy smile, and he sure had one great big old grin on his face.

"Pulling an illegal net," I replied.

"That's right. This is how we do it in the north. We pull it and we pick it all at once."

"That's not quite how they do it down here," I replied looking at the mess. "What do you take to court if the guy pleads not guilty? What do you tell the magistrate if you have to measure it?"

"Court? Who said anything about court?" he asked.

"Well, you're going to charge him, aren't you?"

"With what," he laughed. "There's no evidence."

Well, he was certainly right about that, I thought. Now, I was starting to wonder what I was going to tell the guy who thought I should be shot. I didn't figure he'd be too happy about his net.

"What do we do now?" I asked.

"I'll unhook the lines," he replied. "And you can go and gather up my supper."

I stood there for a minute, looking at him, at the hole, at the lines devoid of any mesh. Then I looked out across the ice, and there were fish scattered all over.

"You gonna get them fish, or do I have to do everything?" he asked.

I looked back out across the ice. In the distance I could see other fishermen and vehicles. One of them looked to be coming our way. I raced out on the ice and started to grab fish. I knew it was wrong, but I didn't want to be anywhere near here when the owner showed up. I grabbed as many fish as I could hold with the leather mitts on. I raced back to his car. The no nonsense guy had an empty cardboard box in the trunk of his car. How convenient, I thought, as I tossed the fish in. One landed on the side of the box and bounced out. I left it, lying on the floor, and raced back for another load.

"Throw them in the box," yelled the no nonsense

guy. "You're gonna stink up my car."

Now, it was my turn to ignore him as I gathered the remaining fish. I fired them into the trunk and jumped into the passenger seat.

As we drove away, the only evidence of our visit was the two lines that stretched out across the ice like two dead snakes. Evidence. Evidence. I kept thinking what evidence was there that would put me at this scene. The leather mitts, I thought, leather mitts covered with whitefish scales. I would have to burn my leather mitts.

Oh man, but I couldn't wait to leave for training school and the sooner the better.

JESS

"Very well, the sentence of this court, is that you pay a fine of 100 dollars ...."

"I'll pay," Jess interrupted. "I'll pay."

"And in default of payment, you will serve ...," the magistrate hesitated. He stared at Jess then continued. "And in default of payment, you will serve one day in jail."

I was watching the accused carefully as the sentence was handed down.

"One day in jail," I snorted, but quietly and to the RCMP constable sitting next to me. "He won't even have to go to jail. This appearance will be his day. He'll be free to go."

Jess' court appearance had taken less then 10 minutes and was a far cry from his previous appearance before the magistrate. I could remember that day and the first day I met him. It was early winter on the prairie and the weather had turned cold. The drop in temperature had been enough to freeze everything solid. Lake Newell was no exception. A layer of ice, about three inches of the stuff, covered its surface. The surface of the lake was like a sheet of glass, a giant mirror, that stretched to the west, as far as the eye could see. Except for the holes dug by the fishermen, there was not a ripple or blemish on it.

I was on patrol, checking anglers, but, unlike many of the anglers, I was not nearly as brave or adventurous as they were. I confined my driving to the dry frozen prairie, around the lakeshore, good old terra firma. They, on the other hand, had all driven their cars and trucks out on the ice. Like I said, I was not nearly as adventurous; in fact, I was scared. I didn't trust the ice and I certainly didn't want to have to tell the Powers-that-be that I had parked my trusty green station wagon on the bottom of the lake. Being a devout coward, I made a decision. I would only check those fishermen who were close enough to the shore that I could walk to them.

During my travels, inching along the edge of the lake, I finally spotted a group of anglers who, as luck would have it, were not too far from shore. I could walk to them easily and check their licences and gear. My first step on the giant mirror was very tentative. The ice moaned, groaned and cracked. I hesitated. I looked out at the fishermen. If the ice was thick enough to hold them and their vehicles, surely it had to be thick enough to hold me. But it was making some strange noises, that sounded suspiciously like ice about to break and swallow poor Bobby Adams.

"Careful, now," one of the fishermen yelled. "The ice is pretty thin over there. If I was you, I'd test 'er real good before I came any closer." His comments were followed by a chorus of laughter from the others.

"Laugh, you mothers," I mumbled. Then I took another slow step, sliding my foot ahead on the ice before I put all my weight on it. Again, the ice moaned, groaned and cracked with my weight. I should have come out here and tested the ice when there was no one around, I cursed to myself. But I was here now, and committed. I couldn't turn back.

"You be careful, sonny," cautioned the voice again. "I don't want to have to come over there and fish you out now." There was more laughter. There was no doubt that I was the source of amusement, providing the group with a healthy dose of humor. They were killing themselves laughing, while I was dying a thousand deaths, testing the ice with every step, as I pussyfooted my way across the ice.

Finally, after what seemed to be an agonizing lifetime, I reached the first guy. Nervously, I looked around me. All but one of the fishermen were using rods, reels and line. Some even had fancy tip-ups. The odd man out and the two kids fishing next to him didn't seem to belong with this group. They looked more like the poor country cousins. Their clothes were well worn and displayed many patches. Their coats seemed too thin for the crisp chilly air. I looked at the sad eyes of the kids. They looked like they could use a good meal.

But it was the poor country cousin who kept up the verbal cautioning, the chiding, while the kids had stood silent, watching. The poor country cousin and the kids used only hand lines. They did not have even a wooden stick.

I checked the licences and looked at the equipment of the other fishermen. All the while, the poor country cousin must have found my actions humorous, for he continued to crack more jokes about my abilities out on the ice. Some of his jokes weren't that complimentary but then, I knew, most of what he was saying had a good smattering of truth in it. I was new to the game, and I was scared spitless. I was a prime target for the butt of his jokes.

When I approached the poor country cousin, I had checked all the licences but his.

"What's your name, sir?" I asked.

"Folks call me Jess," he replied.

"I see. And tell me, Jess, do you live around here?"

"I do. Over by the edge of the lake," he replied proudly.

"And the kids, sir. Who do the kids belong to?"

"They're my kids," he replied.

"That's what I thought," I replied. I looked at the kids and, for some reason, I couldn't bring myself to ask Jess, the jokester, if I could see his angling licence. It was just one of those feelings. Everything about him told me he didn't have a licence, but a little voice, deep inside my head said: 'Don't ask the question. You don't want to hear his answer.' Then, I heard myself saying: "Well sir, you have yourself a good day." There were more cautioning words, bursts of laughter, moaning, groaning and cracking ice, as I retreated toward the safety of the shoreline. Not till I reached the frozen prairie did I breathe easy. Finally, my knees stopped shaking and I was able to walk with some degree of confidence. Then I turned and looked back at the group.

I met Jess and his children many times on the lake during the winter. They could be found angling or commercial fishing. They could be found at any time of the day, and on any day of the week. Not only did they live at the lake, but I suspected they lived off the lake. Every time I saw him, the little voice told me: 'If you don't want to hear the answer, don't ask the question.' The sight of him and his family, fishing for their supper, always brought back many memories. Memories of another family, in another time, at another place. Memories of a family that also had to struggle to eke out a meagre existence. A memory that I would keep forever.

I was about 10 years old and living on the stump farm when I saw a moose walk out of the bush south of the house.

"Dad. Dad. There's a moose. There's a moose," I yelled as I charged towards the house.

Dad came out of the house on a hot July evening.

"Whoa now, slow down, son. What's all the yelling and hollering about?" Dad was in no hurry. He was never in a hurry.

"There's a moose. There's a moose," I repeated excitedly and waved in the direction of the muskeg south of the house.

"Okay. Okay. Slow down and show me where he is," Dad replied calmly.

"He was right there in the muskeg. But I think he walked across the road," I puffed all out of breath from running. I was still pointing to the muskeg south of the house.

"I don't see anything," Dad replied skeptically as he surveyed the willows and swamp spruce. "Are you sure you saw a moose."

"Yeah, I did. It was right there, Dad. Right there in the muskeg and he was walking towards the road."

"Okay, then. We'll just go have a little look see," Dad answered and returned to the house. A couple of minutes later he came out carrying his rifle. It was his 45-70 Winchester single shot. It was an old rifle, just like the ones the US Cavalry used in the Western movies.

"You stay here, now. I don't want anyone following me," Dad cautioned. We all stood by the house and watched. Dad crossed the yard and entered the edge of the muskeg. I wanted to yell and tell him he was right where the moose had been when he suddenly turned and ran across the road. It was unusual to see my Dad run.

The whole family stood by the door at the front of the house. We watched and we waited. The only sound was the hum of mosquitos.

"KABOOM." The sound of the rifle shot exploded, shattering the peace of the summer evening. I jumped and my heart beat with excitement at the loud report.

"Did he shoot it, Mom?" I asked.

"I don't know," she replied. "I guess we'll have to

wait and see."

After waiting for what seemed to be a very long time, I asked again: "Do you think he got it."

"I'm not sure," she answered. Then her voice changed. "In the house quick. C'mon everyone, get in the house."

"Why?"

"Because someone's coming down the road. That's why," Mom replied anxiously. "Now get in the house." Mom meant business and, when she meant business, we all listened. We hustled our little butts into the house and over to the kitchen window. A lone figure emerged slowly walking down the road. He stopped and looked at the house, then continued on.

We all held our breath as the heavy-set man walked slowly past the spot where Dad had crossed the road. On he walked, south, past the muskeg and out of sight.

"That nosy old bugger," Mom whispered, half to herself. Then the figure reappeared and came slowly up the road. He would walk a few steps, then stop and listen, walk a few more steps and listen again. It took forever for him to walk past our house again.

"Who is it, Mom?"

"It's that old bachelor who has moved into a shack on the south end of Grandfather's property," she replied. "Oh, I hope your father doesn't decide to come out of the bush right now," she prayed. "That old bugger will probably report him to the game warden. I told Grandfather not to let him move in there. He's going to be trouble."

Dad didn't come out of the bush for a long time. It

was well after dark when he finally returned to the house. There was blood on his shirt and pants. He had a big old grin on his face that went from ear to ear. He had a heart and liver in his hands. Tomorrow, there would be fresh liver and onions on the table.

"The old bachelor was poking around right after the shot was fired," Mom mentioned to Dad. Mom was worried.

"I'll have a little chat with him in the morning," Dad reassured her. "Don't worry. Right now, I need some clean clothes and a good wash. Bob get a bucket of cold water and wash this liver," he instructed me. "Then I want you to put it in the pail, in the well, to cool overnight."

"Where's the rest of the animal?" Mom asked.

"It's in the bush behind the barn. I've got it all cut into pieces. You'll have to can it tomorrow."

Next morning bright and early Mom rustled us all out of bed. Dad had already eaten when we came into the kitchen. He picked up his lunch pail, wished us all a good day and left for Edson. Dad had been lucky enough to get a couple of weeks work on a construction crew.

There was already one leg of the moose on the table and she was busy cutting it up. Three piles of moose meat were building and with each cut she would add to one of them. There were small steaks, stew meat and trimmings for hamburger.

"Bobby, as soon as you've had breakfast, you can start to grind the hamburger."

I didn't relish the thought of my day. Until that

moose was gone, I was going to be standing by the chair, where the hand grinder was screwed to the seat. It was a job that required no brains, picking up a couple of small pieces of meat at a time, drop them in the feeder and crank the handle. Pick up a couple of more, drop them in, and crank the handle. Oh, it was going to be one long tedious day.

The inside of the kitchen and the house was like an oven. I was wringing wet with sweat and looked forward to the occasional break.

"Okay, Bobby, you can get rid of this bone now." Mom would say when she had finished trimming every last bit of meat from it. I would then take every bone and throw it away, scattering them out in the muskeg.

When Mom wasn't cutting meat, she was canning it. Hamburgers were fried, along with the stew meat and the steaks. These she would stuff into glass sealers, keeping each cut separate, then they were put into a hot water bath and canned. It was a long, tiring process, but she never complained. The smell of cooking moose meat was everywhere.

Everything was humming right along, we had a real production line going, when suddenly Mom stopped.

"Oh my lord, no," Mom whispered. "The game warden's here." She was white as a ghost, looking out the window. I rushed to her side in time to see the truck turn into the driveway. It didn't require a sign, the forestry green color told everyone who it was.

"Quickly, Bobby, wash your hands and get outside," Mom whispered hurriedly, as she shed her blood-splattered apron and tossed it into the bedroom. She rapidly washed her hands and raced for the door. I was right behind her.

The truck rolled to a stop at the back of the house and an elderly man in a uniform stepped out. Holy cow, I thought to myself as I looked at the size of him. The game warden's a giant.

"Good day, Mrs. Adams," he greeted Mom.

Mom's weak "Hello," barely squeaked from her lips.

"And how are you on this fine day?" he asked. On his face was the biggest smile.

"I'm just fine on this hot day," Mom replied and managed a very weak smile on her sweat-stained face.

"We're fighting a fire just south of here and I was wondering if I might get a drink of cold water? Would that be possible?" he asked. "I understand that your well has some of the finest water in these parts."

"Of course. Bobby go get the man a nice cold drink from the well," Mom suddenly found her voice and barked the order at me.

"If you don't mind, I'll come along too," the warden offered. "I can use the walk and it is a beautiful day. Isn't it a beautiful day, Mrs. Adams?" he asked. "A person wouldn't want to be tied up in the house on a day like today, now would they?" he added.

"Certainly not on a day like this," Mom replied, her voice wavering as we turned towards the well. The well that had the ropes dangling down the inside. Ropes with pails, pails containing perishable foods. Like butter, milk, meat and fresh moose liver and heart.

I had never seen Mom so nervous. She kept wringing her hands in her skirt as we walked past the house towards the well. There was a delicious smell in the air: the smell of cooking moose meat. Nothing smells better than moose meat, I thought, as we walked past the kitchen. The unmistakable aroma drifted through the open window.

"Bobby, go draw the water," Mom ordered. She picked up the pace, but the game warden paused right outside the window. He sniffed long and loud, inhaling a huge breath. Then, he looked skyward before he followed us to the well.

I raced ahead and opened the lid to the well. As quick as I could, I dropped the water pail with the rope attached, right past the pail with the liver and heart, into the water. Splash. I never realized before how loud that splash was until the pail hit the water. My hands were a blur as I hoisted the pail up and over the side. Mom was sure moving a lot slower then she had been earlier. I had plenty of time to slam the lid down, hiding the evidence, before Mom and the warden arrived. I sat the water pail on the well cover then grabbed the dipper. I dipped it into the ice cold water and handed it to him.

He took the dipper and took a long look at the clear water before taking a big drink.

"Ahhh," he sighed. He lifted his head towards the sky and closed his eyes, savoring the moment. "Now that's what I call a good drink of water. Cold and pure. Just like I was told." He helped himself to another dipper full then walked over to the fence still holding the dipper. He paused for a moment, then climbed the fence and sat on the top rail. He was an expert at climbing fences with a dipper full of water, he never spilled a single drop.

"You know, there's nothing quite like a cool drink of pure fresh well water on a hot summer's day," he said to no one in particular as he drank the dipper dry.

If he thinks it's a hot summer's day out here, he should be in the house, turning the meat grinder, I thought. Then he'd know what a hot summer's day really was.

We all stood there watching him, waiting. What was he going to do next? Does he know about the moose. He just looked up at the sky. The dipper hung loose in his hand. He was so calm and relaxed it scared the dickens out of me. What else had someone told him about the stump farm?

"Could I please have another dipper of that water?" he asked, breaking the silence. Then he held the dipper out to me.

I took the dipper and dipped it into the pail. I'll bet he's going to drink all the water in the pail and then say that he'll draw the next pailful. That was it. He knew that, down in that well, there was another pail. A pail containing the moose heart and liver. The old game warden was sure one cool customer.

I looked at Mom. She wasn't cool. She was sweating and busy twisting her dress. I wanted to tell her that she was going to tear her dress if she continued to twist it so hard.

The old warden, the cool dude, seemed to be enjoying himself. He just sat there, enjoying the day and when he spoke, he spoke only of the fresh cool water and the beautiful hot day. I handed him the dipper full of water.

"You know, when I was a boy growing up on a farm in southern Saskatchewan, I used to love to sit on the fence and watch the clouds go by on nice summer days. Days just like this one. You don't mind if I just sit and rest for a spell and watch the clouds drift by, do you, Mrs. Adams?" he asked, still looking at the sky. There was hardly a cloud anywhere, but if he could see them that was fine with us. Looking up was fine, looking down would be disastrous.

"No, not at all. You just make yourself real comfortable," Mom answered. "I think I'll just sit down by the fence myself." She dropped to the ground beside a fence post real quick like before her knees gave out. "Yes, it is nice just to sit and watch the clouds roll by," she agreed. But, she never looked toward the sky. She never took her eyes off the old warden.

We all sat down. The warden looking up at the sky, the rest of us looking at the warden. Every once in a while, I would steal a look at the sky. But, I had to admit, the old warden's eyes were better than mine. For the life of me, I couldn't find the clouds.

"I think I'll have one more drink of the water," the old warden said suddenly. Without any warning he jumped off the fence and strode over to the well. We held our breath as he took another dipper full of water and guzzled it down. "Mrs. Adams, that truly is mighty fine water," he sighed. Then he turned and started walking toward the house, toward the smell of cooking moose. He was headed straight toward the door. The door that hid the moose that was in various stages of being butchered and canned.

We, too, were on our feet not saying a word as we followed right behind him. Once more there was the overpowering smell of cooking moose meat and it grew stronger with every step toward the house. Again, the old game warden paused outside the kitchen window. He drew another deep breath, then sighed before he turned and ambled around the side of the building to his truck.

"I'd truly like to stay and chat for a while, but I better be getting back into town," he informed Mom. "I have a lot of supplies to pick up and haul back out to the fire. Did you know that hot days like this are real bad for fires?" he asked.

None of us did. We just stood there shaking our heads "no" and watched him.

"Thanks again for the drink, folks," he smiled. "Like I said, Mrs. Adams, there's nothing better then good drink of cold well water on a hot day," he paused. "It always tastes so fresh and pure. I find it really picks me up. Yessirree, there's nothing better."

He climbed into the cab of his truck then hesitated before hollering back. "You take it easy now, Mrs. Adams. It's too hot a day to be working very hard. A person should be working outside on a day like this." He gave us a big friendly smile, he waved and drove out of the yard.

"Do you know the warden?" I asked Mom as soon as he had driven out of the yard and was out of earshot.

"No, I don't. I've never seen him before," she answered.

"But, he knew you. He kept calling you Mrs. Adams."

"Maybe he knows Daddy."

"Yeah. Maybe he knows Dad."

"Okay. Let's get back to work. We're a long way from being finished," she sighed. Now Mom looked real tired.

"But Mom, the warden told us not to work too hard that we should be outside on a hot day like this," I argued. I had to agree with the old warden. It was a lot nicer outside then in. We hadn't yet moved toward the house, and already I was dreading the handle of the meat grinder and the heat from the cookstove.

"Well," Mom sighed. "The game warden doesn't have a moose to cut up or can, either. C'mon now, let's go. We've wasted enough time," she sighed again. "As it is, we'll probably be canning moose all night."

The thought of the stump farm, the poached moose and the game warden were vivid in my memory. With those thoughts, I knew why I hadn't brought myself to ask Jess the question. There were a lot of similarities between Dad and Jess, I thought. Jess was certainly louder. However, both men knew hard times. Dad had always done whatever it took to make sure his family had food, clothing and shelter. I could see that Jess was doing the same. Both did what they had to do for their families. I was feeling pretty good about my decision.

The first time I stopped to check Jess and the kids pulling a net, I stopped short. All fishermen fished three nets, but not Jess. He fished only one. I watched in disbelief at the tattered, torn mesh they were pulling through the hole and spreading onto the ice. It was an old cotton rag. There were holes big enough to drive the green station wagon through. And the fish he caught, lake whitefish, were the smallest fish I had ever seen. Once more, I could not ask the question, but I did offer a word of caution.

"If I were you, sir, I think I'd measure that net before next season. Them cotton nets, they have a tendency to shrink during the summer," I said.

"Can't afford another net," Jess replied.

One day in late winter, I had another meeting with Jess. The ice was much thicker now, probably about three feet thick. I had spent the whole winter on the lake, checking anglers and commercial fishermen. I was no longer the greenhorn. I was confident, secure and sure of myself. On three feet of ice, I had no fear.

Jess and his kids were angling in the vicinity of a fish shack. The shack was a new edition to the scene. It had not been there on my last trip. It appeared that the shack was brand spanking new. The boards were not painted, nor were they weathered. Something new, like the shack, was a challenge for an inquisitive mind like mine. My curiosity dictated that I had to check it and its occupant.

It had snowed about a half an inch overnight and the lake was covered in a new white blanket. I stopped the green station wagon beside Jess and stepped out onto the fresh snow.

"Who got ambitious and set up the new fish shack?"

I asked him.

"Who knows?" he replied. He shrugged his shoulders and turned his back on me.

"Anybody in it?"

"I don't know," he mumbled. "I guess you'll have to go see for yourself."

"I guess I will," I replied. There were a lot of tracks in the fresh snow around the holes where Jess was fishing. There were also a lot of old holes that had been used for angling and commercial fishing. In the fresh snow, the holes were all visible. Each was identified by an indented circle in the blanket of fresh snow. It was impossible to tell which ones had been there for a month or a day. There were no foot prints in the snow on any of the old holes. But, there was one set of tracks that led from where Jess was fishing, over to the fish shack. I followed the tracks, being careful not to step on any of the old holes. No sense taking a needless bath. That would only be more material for Jess. I really didn't need to be the butt of more jokes at his expense.

I paused near the front of the door. There was only one set of tracks leading into the shack, none coming out. There was also the tell tale ring of an old fish hole, a large old fish hole, a commercial fish hole, right in front of the door. And in the fresh snow, right in the center of the hole, there was a single foot print. I debated, should I step over it, or should I be so bold as to follow the lead and step in the track. I turned and looked at Jess, but he wasn't interested, he was busy looking out across the lake. It had to be an old hole, I convinced myself, or else the guy in the shack would be at the bottom of the lake. But, being ever cautious, I avoided the potential danger, I leaned over the hole and rapped on the door.

"Anybody home?" I called out. I was greeted with silence. Not a word, not a sound came in response.

"Go on, step in there and have a look around," Jess called out and laughed. "Ain't nobody going to answer you."

I looked back at Jess. Now he had turned back, turned to watch, to see what would happen. I knew, then, that somebody was in the shack, waiting, but why? What was the game?

"Anybody home?" I called again, but still no response. I banged on the side of the shack with my fist and called once more.

"Open the door, or I'm comin' in."

Finally, I reached over and grabbed a strip of leather hanging on the door, I tugged. It was closed tight, and didn't budge. I pushed, the door gave way and I stumbled forward. I was not as careful as I should have been. I lost my balance and fell forward, crashing through the door. I put my overshoe in the same spot where the shoe print appeared in the fresh snow and I heard the unmistakable cracking of thin ice and the splash of water.

"What the ..." I yelled as my foot dropped away. I clutched the little strip of leather on the door tighter, hoping to stop my fall, but it pulled off. I grabbed for something else, there was nothing else. The footprint in the fresh snow covering the old hole was not safe. It was not as old as it appeared. Under the snow, there was only a thin skim of ice, just enough to hold the snow. The hole had probably been dug the day before. My overshoe, with my shoe and foot still inside, was headed for the bottom of the lake and I had visions of following it. I feared that I was going to be seeing the ice and the hole from the watery side.

My legs were taking different trips. One was busy going south, getting soaking wet and taking a trip down, the other was skidding off on a trip to the west. The leg going west probably would have gone farther, but the knee objected, knees were not meant to go west when the rest of the body is headed south. Thanks to the obstinate knee, the leg headed for the bottom of the lake was dropping further into the hole. While my legs were taking unscheduled trips, my arms too were busy, they were flailing around wildly trying to find something, anything to hang onto.

While all this was going on, for some reason, my head decided to have a look inside the fish shack. It shot forward, toward the open door, but the balky knee going west forced the rest of my body east. My head changed directions and slammed into the door jamb.

My leg, traveling south seemed determined to pull the rest of me through the hole. Many things flashed through my mind and I thought I was a goner, until I got a hand on the door jamb. I finally, stopped the descent and came to rest sprawled out on the ice with one leg dangling in the lake. I breathed a sigh of relief. Thankful that most of me was still on the top of the ice. I lay there for a second to get my breath and my bearings. The leg down the hole had this very cold, soaking wet, wet-to-the-skin feeling. The leg on the ice had these horrible little shooting pains coming from the vicinity of the knee. My head had a numb feeling that I could not really discern.

In the background I could hear Jess just splitting a gut.

"I can see you certainly didn't learn anything about ice over the winter, did ya?" he laughed.

Slowly, I pulled myself out of the hole and struggled to my feet. I looked down at the cold, icy lake water that streamed down my pant leg. I watched as it drained back into the hole. Steam began to lift from my leg and drift into the winter air. My first thought was to return to the warmth and comfort of the green station wagon. I never thought that station wagon would look so good.

Then I looked over at Jess. He was still standing at his fish hole. He had not taken one step to help me. In fact, it was obvious, he was enjoying the whole scene.

When I looked at Jess, I suddenly had a real twinge of guilt. How in the world could I have compared this man with my father, I thought. The only similarities were that they were poor. My dad was a kind, loving man. He would never have set someone up to hurt himself, and he would never have laughed at someone who was hurt.

I tried a tentative step. My knee was wonky and just about killing me, but wonky knee or not, I walked. Water, cold lake water, slopped out of one overshoe with each step. The other overshoe seemed to have a mind of its own and wanted to swing out, away from my body, each time I moved it. I walked, or rather hobbled, sloshing, gurgling and shuffling, over to Jess. I would have made it over to him if I had to crawl. I was ready to hear the answer. Steam continued to rise from the one leg and the pain in the other, brought tears to my eyes as I stood before him.

"Did you set that up?" I asked.

"You should have seen yourself," Jess, chuckled. "That's the best laugh I've had for years. You sure did put on quite a show."

Yes, if there was ever any doubt, it was gone. Today, right now, I was ready to hear the answer.

"Could I please see your angling licence, sir?" I asked as politely as I could.

That stopped him and wiped the smile from his face.

"You know I don't have a licence," he replied. "I've never had one."

"No, sir, I didn't know that," I answered. I reached over and took his stick and line. "You sir, are going to be charged with fishing without an angling licence."

When Jess appeared in court, he dragged his whole family up the stairs and into the courtroom. I appeared as well. I dragged my leg with a cast from the hip to the bottom of my foot, up the stairs into the courtroom. As was the custom of the day, the magistrate, His Honor, was seated at the front of the room. His desk, a table with a chair behind, resembled the tables with chairs that the police, prosecutors and defense counsel used.

Court had not yet been opened when Jess decided to address the bench.

"Go ahead," he snorted. "Send me to jail. I'm not paying any fine. You guys think you can look after my family, you go ahead and put me in jail. Then you can feed my family."

"Sit down," roared His Honor and the whole courtroom shook. The magistrate was a very healthy, huge individual who had only recently been appointed to the bench. I had heard it said that he resembled a bulldog, and one should be careful of his bite. I, personally, found him to be a very jovial individual who loved to laugh and tell jokes. But not in his courtroom. Here he was all business and, as I had learned, he certainly did have a loud bark. I for one never tempted him for, having heard the bark, I was afraid of the bite.

"You can have your say when court is open and you've been called," His Honor barked.

There had been quite a scene at the back of the court room until His Honor had barked. After that, you could have heard a pin drop. No one spoke. All was quiet until court was finally opened. Then Jess was called forth and the charge was read.

"How do you plead?" asked His Honor.

"Guilty," shouted Jess. "Now you can send me to jail and you can feed my family."

"Do you have anything else to say?" asked the magistrate.

"I told you, you can send me to jail and you can feed my family," shouted Jess.

His Honor sat there eyeing Jess. It seemed like an eternity before he finally spoke. Then in a very calm, quiet, even tone he said.

"The sentence of this court is that you pay a fine of

one dollar and in default of payment you will spend 30 days in jail. Can you pay the fine?"

"One dollar," I snorted, but not too loud for I didn't want to incur the wrath of the magistrate. Instead, I mumbled my displeasure to the RCMP constable sitting next to me. "He tried to drown me and all he gets is one dollar." I couldn't believe what I had just heard.

"I told you I'm going to jail," Jess sneered defiantly. "I wouldn't pay you one cent. You can feed my family till I get out."

"As you wish," replied His Honor. Jess was led away by the RCMP. Rather than pay the dollar, Jess left his family sitting in the courtroom and defiantly strode from the courtroom with his RCMP escort. Jess went to jail.

I spent a lot of time on the lake that summer. I checked hundreds of anglers and boaters. The following winter I checked more anglers and commercial fishermen, but it was almost a year before Jess and I crossed paths again. It was during the commercial fishing season and once more he was using the ratty old cotton net. The whitefish still looked small coming out of the hole.

"Well, sir, I trust that you took my advice and measured that net before you put it in the water this year, because today I'm going to measure your nets," I stated.

Once more, Jess appeared in the courtroom in Brooks. This time, he walked up the steps to the courtroom by himself. The magistrate was seated behind the table when he entered the courtroom, but

Jess went silently to the back of the courtroom and sat down. I limped up the steps to the court room, the knee still gave me a little trouble, particularly when I had to climb steps. I sat down at the table beside the RCMP constable.

Jess stood silently when his name was called.

"You are charged with fishing with a small-mesh net. How do you plead to the charge?" asked His Honor.

"Guilty," replied Jess.

"Do you wish to say anything on your own behalf?" There was no response. Again His Honor studied Jess for a couple of minutes, then continued. "Very well, the sentence of this court, is that you pay a fine of 100 dollars ...."

"I'll pay," Jess interrupted. "I'll pay."

"And in default of payment, you will serve ...," again the magistrate hesitated. He stared at Jess, then continued. "And in default of payment, you will serve ... one day in jail."

"One day in jail," I snorted, but quietly and to the RCMP constable sitting next to me. "He won't even have to go to jail. This appearance will be his day. He's free to go."

"Can you pay the fine now, or do you wish time to pay?" His Honor asked.

"I'll pay now," Jess replied and hastily dug his wallet out of his worn pants pocket.

Now, I knew for sure there were no similarities between Dad and Jess. Dad never had a 100 dollars in his wallet in his life.

GOOSE BANDING

RRRRRRRROOOOWWWRRRRREEEEEEEEEEEE.
The sound of the racing motor roared across the prairie.
But it was quickly drowned out by the high-pitched
whine of rapidly spinning tires cutting through the
muddy bottom of a wet sticky alkali slough.

"Maybe we better go help them," I foolishly
suggested, forgetting that I was with the pranksters that
had sent them over there in the first place. It had always
been my experience that, when a person got stuck, you
went out and helped, but my little comment just
brought howls of laughter from the crew. Obviously I
had just cracked a funny.

"Oh, yeah. Stuck in an alkali slough with mud up to
your butt ought to hold those two all right," I chuckled
weakly, trying to recover from my little slip of the
tongue. "You know, guys, on second thought, maybe
I'll just get back to work."

This was my first day of helping the Ducks Unlimited folks with their goose banding program. And what a day it was shaping up to be. What an experience; certainly not what I had expected. But, then, I really wasn't sure what I expected. I had previously met several of the crew and should have had an inkling of what was to come. They were jokers. As I bent down to pick another handful of aluminum rods, I reminded myself that it would probably be better if I just kept my mouth shut and my eyes and ears open.

There was quite a collection of bodies that showed up at the DU office first thing that morning. There were several DU staff, from Brooks, some from Strathmore, there were some students hired on for summer jobs, there were a couple of volunteers from town, there was a biologist and there was one hairy-arsed fish cop. It was a term I had overheard some of the crew use when they affectionately referred to me.

I quickly found out that the rest of the crew were practical jokesters as well and nobody, but nobody, was immune. When you became part of the banding crew, you became a candidate for the butt of a joke. The question was not *Would someone get you?* it was only a matter of who and when.

George, Mr. Ducks Unlimited from Strathmore, was easily identified. He had an easy-going manner, he laughed and talked a lot. I'd have to say that George was also the biggest practical joker on site. George was the guy most likely to succeed in getting everybody, before the day was out. It was George who had sent the boys into the alkali slough.

George was a bundle of energy, a man who really knew his business. And all the while he worked, he talked and joked and laughed. George was fun to be around and he kept the job interesting. He also kept everyone on their toes. A small error on someone's behalf was certain to become the subject of a good-natured barb from George. He was quick on the pick-up and never missed a chance.

There were a couple of young bucks on the crew who seemed to be enjoying themselves immensely. They were loud and boisterous fun-loving boys, real hellions actually, and they were out to make their mark. They seemed to be vying for the title of the best pranksters on the crew. The lake and the prairie for miles around reverberated with the sounds of their voices and laughter. But not everyone seemed to appreciate their boyish enthusiasm.

The old banding vets were concerned about the effect of all the commotion and activity on the birds. And they were keeping a close eye on the large raft of geese out on the lake. There were geese of all sizes and all ages. The geese had moved to the center of the lake as our motorcade rolled across the prairie and stopped on the lake shore. Upon our arrival, the geese began to move away from the center of the lake. Slowly, they were edging toward the far shore. One man, who appeared to be a newcomer to the banding crew, and his vehicle were dispatched to the far side of the lake.

"Take the long way around and stay out of sight until you get behind the hill," he was instructed. "Park your truck on the hill. Right up on top, in plain view.

Then you get out and walk around so the geese can see you. We don't want them birds taking off across the prairie before we get set up." Following instructions the truck moved away from the lake. Driving cautiously, the driver hardly raised any dust as the truck disappeared into the prairie. A short time later, it reappeared, and stopped right smack dab on top of the hill. The driver got out and, in plain sight, for all to see, he walked slowly back and forth. The geese began to drift back toward the middle of the lake.

The two young rambunctious goose banders were next on the list.

"You two think you can follow orders?" George asked them.

"You bet we can," one of the replied. "You name it. We'll do it."

"Okay, then. You're gonna stop the geese from heading off across the prairie in the other direction," they were told. "You take your truck and head off due west. Just across the rise here, you'll see this large white area. Cut across it and hit the hill on the far side. Park on top and move around the vehicle so the geese can see you. Understand?"

"Yeah, we understand," replied one with a big smart grin on his kisser.

"Don't forget, cut across the white area now and head straight for the top of the hill. Hurry up, get goin'. We don't want them geese to get away on us." The two young bucks were laughing and howling as they raced for their truck.

"I'll drive," laughed one.

"Over my dead body," howled the other.

"You two get your butts movin', now," roared one of the crew. "If we lose those geese, it'll be over both your dead bodies. Now move it." The two young bucks wrestled and jostled at the side of the truck until one succeeded in getting into the truck behind the wheel. He started the engine and revved the motor while the other raced around the front to get in. With the motor racing, the driver let out the clutch. The wheels spun, dust, dirt and grass spewed out behind. In a spray of debris and a cloud of dust, the truck roared off across the prairie, heading for the distant hill. The cloud of dust, billowing up from their spinning tires, marked their progress.

"Idiots," chuckled George and the crew laughed.

I, too, was new to the banding crew. I looked around to see if there was a third hill on the horizon. Since it appeared that new crew members drew point duty on some distant hill, I thought for sure, somewhere out there on the bald headed prairie, there had to be a hill with my name on it. But, the crew did not wait for the second truck to get into place. As the cloud of dust rose in the distance, they began to set up for banding.

First item on the agenda, for all the remaining goose banders, was to don the appropriate goose banding attire. I don't mind admitting that I was a little more than amazed when each of the crew dropped their drawers, then proceeded to peel off their shorts. Before my startled eyes was the banding crew, naked as the day they were born. I was equally relieved when out of the backs of trucks and from the trunks of cars came boxes and bags with the banders' clothes. And, what an assortment of clothes it was. Ratty tattered old pants were the order of the day. Some had long legs. Some had short legs. Some had no legs at all and looked like tattered tutus. All were torn and ripped. All were dirty and most were damp. All smelled to high heaven. Oh, but the goose banding crew was a rag tag lot. Hiding behind a vehicle, I hastened to get into the old pair of pants I brought along, but my old pants looked like suit pants compared to the crew. None, but me it seemed, had the sense to be wearing any shorts under this unusual array of apparel.

The crew cringed and cursed as they wriggled their way into their wet smelly duds. All, but George, he was in fine form as he pulled on an old pair of pants that had more holes in them then Swiss cheese. George provided the color commentary on every member of the crew.

Most of those present had banded together for many years and each had their own job. Without a word of instruction, each man set about the task of setting up the goose trap. Well, everyone but me. I didn't have a clue what my job was. Suddenly, there were men in the water and men strung out along the shore. Rods and nets were being strung out all over the prairie. I stood there with my hands in my pockets, not sure which way to turn or who to help. I felt like a spare tire.

"Hey, you. Fish cop. There's no free rides here," someone yelled at me. "Grab some of them banding rods and help set up the water wing," I was instructed.

"Right," I responded, and reached for a handful of

168

aluminum rods. Each was about six feet long and light as a feather. I could probably get about a dozen in each hand.

RRRRRRRROOOOWWWRRRRREEEEEEEEEEEE.

I stopped what I was doing and stood up. I stared at the cloud of dust that billowed up over the small hill. Only moments earlier, the half-ton truck, with wheels spinning and motor racing, had bounced across the prairie. Up the hillside they went, over the top then disappeared from sight. I listened and again I heard the sound of the motor, it roared angrily before it was finally drowned out by the high-pitched sound of the tires screaming as they fought their way through mud.

"It sounds to me like those two guys got stuck," I remarked to the goose banding crew, assembled on the lake shore. They, pranksters all, had been working, laughing and joking, but now they all stopped and for a second silently stared out across the prairie. Each man faced to the west, the direction of the sound. The sound of a half ton truck hopelessly stuck in an alkali slough.

"It sure does, doesn't it?" someone laughed breaking the silence.

"Well, that's good," warbled another. "Maybe now we can get some work done in peace."

"Yeah, I'd say that should keep them out of our hair for a while," chuckled a third.

"Maybe we better go help them," I foolishly suggested, forgetting that I was with the pranksters that had sent them over there in the first place. It had always been my experience that, when a person got stuck, you went out and helped, but my little comment just brought howls of laughter from the crew. Obviously I had just cracked a funny.

"Oh, yeah. Stuck in an alkali slough with mud up to your butt ought to hold those two all right," I chuckled weakly, trying to recover from my little slip of the tongue. "You know, guys, on second thought, maybe I'll just get back to work."

My eyes were on the cloud of dust, but my hand continued toward the rods. I grabbed a handful and stood up. Then, I realized, one of the rods had wrapped itself around my hand and was wriggling vigorously.

"What the … Jeezz," I barely whimpered. My heart skipped a beat, I lost my voice and I instantly broke into a cold sweat on the hot day. I cursed and jumped back like I had just grabbed a hot poker.

Banding rods flew in every direction. Every banding rod but one and that one,I feared, was a rattlesnake. I could tell by the feel of it that it was a monstrous snake and it had coiled itself lightly around my hand. Its head was twisting and turning trying to sink its fangs into my arm. But, it wasn't there for long, with a mighty heave, I flung that mother to the ground and was about to stomp it into oblivion with my beat up size nine sneakers.

"Here, don't kill it," cautioned a voice right behind me.

"Why not?" I asked. "The bloody thing scared me half to death."

"No. No. Here. Let me have it," he said. "George is just havin' himself too much fun at everyone's expense." Then he smiled at me. "An' George don't like snakes," he added.

I watched as Martin, the man with a big straw hat and hip waders, shuffled over to where the snake had slithered to. He bent over and picked it up by the tail. It wasn't nearly as big as it was a second earlier and it wasn't a dreaded rattler, it was only a little garter snake. The little snake twisted and turned its head from side to side and flicked its black forked tongue at every twist. Slowly, Martin inched his way over to where George was working. Coming up behind the unsuspecting prankster, he lifted the snake over George's right shoulder. I watched in awe as the snake curled up and stared George straight in the eye, flicking his black forked tongue at him. I expected George to yell and jump out of the way. I expected he would have plenty to say to Martin, but George did none of the things I expected. Only one word escaped his lips.

"Agh," George muttered as his knees buckled and he collapsed in a heap on the ground.

The deed accomplished, a nonchalant Martin casually flipped the snake into the grass as if nothing had happened then shuffled back to the pile of banding rods.

"There, that oughtta hold him for a while," he drawled as he picked up a handful of banding rods and waded out into the lake.

I stared in disbelief looking first at Martin then at George. George lay where he fell. There was no movement. I thought that one of the greatest pranksters I had ever known was dead and all because I accidently picked up a little garter snake.

I sighed with relief when I heard a faint voice.

"You got me," I heard George squeak from his position on the ground. "You got me good." Man, but I was happy to hear George squeak because, up to that time, I was quite certain he had squeaked his last.

No one else seemed to notice or care that poor old George had been lying on the ground for some time. Everybody continued to go about their business of setting up the goose trap, just as if nothing had happened. I didn't do much, except watch George. I was even more relieved when I saw him slowly drag himself to his feet and stumble over to his car. George sat out while the rest of the goose trap set up.

RRRRRRRROOOOWWWRRRRREEEEEEEEEEEEE.

Except for the whining tires from the truck indisposed at the alkali slough, silence had descended over the banding site. For some reason, there seemed to have been enough humor for one day.

Finally, in the silence that gripped the crew, a long line of banding rods had been driven into the lake bottom. They stretched from shore out into the lake at an angle and had a heavy black net hanging from them down into the water. It was a formidable wall for a goose. Another row of rods had been pushed into the ground along the shoreline. They, too, had black netting hanging from them. Another wall. Where the two rows of rods and nets came together, there was a large circle of rods and nets – the holding pen. The trap was ready.

Everyone, including myself, was given a job.

RRRRRRRROOOOWWWRRRRREEEEEEEEEEEEE.

Well, everyone that is except the two in the half-ton.

Somewhere, beyond the hill, they were still roaring their motor and spinning their wheels.

To haze the flightless geese into the trap, everyone moved out onto the water, forming a huge arc, like a big fan. The lone outlook walked off the hill and waded into the lake.

"Did you guys realize that the other truck is stuck in an alkali slough?" he asked when he joined the fan of men.

Several of the old vets broke out laughing.

"Yeah, we can hear 'em," one of them chuckled.

I was almost waist-deep in warm lake water when I noticed an unexpected hazer in our midst. To my surprise, wading through the water with the rest of the crew was none other then George. He seemed to have made a remarkable recovery from his face-to-face encounter with the little snake. Ah, yes, I thought. It's hard to keep a good bander down.

For whatever reason, Martin was close to George as we neared the center of the lake. The geese were moving slowly ahead of us, right toward the trap. Everything was unfolding as it should. But, unlike the activities on the shore, out in the lake there was no shortage of directions and instructions. Everyone was being placed and positioned so as to prevent the geese from slipping through a gap in the crew.

"Martin," George suddenly yelled. "Martin, move to your right. There's too big a gap there. They're gonna get by ya." Well, it certainly seemed that George had completely recovered. At least his voice had.

I personally didn't think there was much of a chance

of the birds getting by anybody. They seemed to moving along quite nicely. Martin, still wearing the big straw hat and hip waders, never replied, but silently, without a word of complaint or objection, he did comply with George's instructions. Martin moved to the right.

"More," yelled George again. "You gotta move more to the right. Slow down everyone until Martin gets over there."

There was no need for the instruction to slow down, by now everyone had slowed down and was looking at Martin, waiting until he filled the gap that George had detected. Martin continued to follow George's instructions and moved slowly to the right.

When Martin hesitated, George yelled again. "A couple more steps, Martin." And Martin took a couple more steps. Then there was silence. Out in the lake where Martin had been, was a huge circular ripple and a large straw hat.

"Har Har Har," howled George, as everyone else stared in silence at the spot where Martin disappeared. The large straw hat bobbed around on the surface of the lake like a cork.

"I figured he'd forgotten about that old creek bed," George crowed. The rest of the crew chuckled as Martin came to the surface sputtering and spitting. The score was even.

The geese were still moving and soon the prank was forgotten. The circle of men grew smaller as they neared the mouth of the trap. A thoroughly drenched Martin slogged through the water and the raft of geese moved along in front of them. The geese moved ahead of the crew and reached the water wing of the trap first. Beyond the net, there were no hazers, only open water and freedom. The birds rushed the net, testing every inch of the netting. They poked their beaks at the black banding net, looking for a hole, an opening in their attempt to find an escape route. Their futile efforts and the hazers served only to work them closer to the holding pen. Finally, the birds waddled ashore and funneled into the holding pen.

RRRRRRRROOOOWWWRRRRRREEEEEEEEEEEEE.

Once more the sound of a roaring motor and the whining of the spinning wheels cut through the air as the crew prepared to band the geese. An assortment of ducks that had come along for the swim were now busy dodging and ducking the huge feet of the milling geese.

With the pen full of geese, the banders, the old vets with many years of experience, set about their business. Each, it seemed, had his own job, for they were the permanent banders, the backbone of any banding crew. Everyone else was given directions collecting birds to hand to the banders or for taking down the wings of the trap. I was assigned the task of removing black banding net from the rods and hauling it out of the water, while someone else was busy calling out the number from a leg band.

"Oooww ooooww. I'll tell you boy, that hurts," I heard a familiar voice ring out as I heaved a section of soaking wet netting up on the shore. Looking over at the crew, I noticed him, right there in the middle of the melee, George. It was George who received the birds from the holding pen. In his holey old pants and no shirt, he was kneeling on the ground holding a goose. Actually, the goose was on its back resting on George's lap. Its head was not in sight. Having been victimized in the past by nipping beak, George had tucked the head away between his legs, somewhere down under his butt. It appeared that the goose had objected to this unkind treatment and, with his beak, the goose had goosed George. There was the indisputable reason why a man banding geese should wear shorts, I thought, as I and the rest of the crew roared with laugher.

George was yanking the bird by the neck to remove the wayward beak when the goose attacked again with the only weapons it had left. Its feet. One huge black foot pawed the air helplessly, but the other had snagged a toehold. One huge toe nail was lodged firmly in George's belly button. With a few choice words to the goose, George dislodged the wayward nail and proceeded with his duties.

One had to marvel at how well George handled the birds. Like an old pro, after he flipped the bird over onto its back and stuffed its head and neck between his legs. He expertly tipped the tail down with his little fingers and blew. The feathers separated and bared the goose's bottom. In a maneuver called thumbing the goose, George used his thumbs and index fingers to roll the exposed portion.

"This mean one's a male," he called out, revealing the sex for the recorder and for the benefit for all who were not close enough to see. George was the sexer.

And sometimes the goose had a bonus for the sexer.

If the goose released its bowels at the precise moment the thumbs rolled, goose crap would fly in all directions. It was not long before George himself resembled a large goose dropping.

As the day drew to a close, the last goose was sexed, banded and released. She did not rush to the water with her wings flapping wildly. She was more dignified than that. She stopped long enough to make a defiant honk at the crew. Then, shaking her tail vigorously, she waddled proudly toward the lake. The nets and banding rods had been gathered and stored away for another day. My first day on the goose banding crew was over. Time to head back to town and relax.

RRRRRRRROOOOWWWRRRRREEEEEEEEEEEEE.

But the sound of the whining tires in the alkali slough reminded us all that our work was not yet complete.

"I suppose we'll have to go and collect those two apes," someone groaned.

"Can't we just leave 'em?" someone else chipped in. "We could always pick them up next year."

Everyone turned and faced west, toward the hill and the sound of the whining tires. The dust had long since settled, or drifted off across the prairie, but we all knew where the two wayward boys were. Right where they had spent the entire day. Stuck, smack dab in the middle of the alkali slough, where George had sent them. It could have been such a quiet scene. No one moved.

THE FILM MAKERS

Several folks stopped to stare and more hustled over as I drove, or should I say maneuvered, the old green station wagon up and parked in front of the Brooks Fish & Wildlife Office, my place of work. I sat inside the vehicle and waited for it to settle down before getting out. It rocked and rolled, bounced and wove around for several minutes before finally slowing and settling enough for me to make an exit. The gathering crowd watched the wildly gyrating vehicle in disbelief.

"Anyone want to buy a good, well, used station wagon?" I asked as I planted my feet on the ground. "I guarantee you, it's the most beautiful ride you'll ever have. This is the closest you'll ever get to floating on a cloud." For effect, I placed one finger on the front fender and pushed down. Once more, the car responded by rocking up and down, from side to side and I'm sure from corner to corner. "Yes sir," I smiled.

"She's just like floating on a cloud." I grinned.

"You hit something?" asked one old timer, who walked over and put his pinky on the other fender and sent the old car into another round of gyrations.

"Just the prairie," I smiled. "Just the old bald-headed, flat, see for-forever, plain old prairie.

"Looks like you sure did a number on the old girl," he whistled. "I'd sure like to be a fly on the wall when you try and explain this one."

"I'll bet you would," I laughed. "I'll just bet you would."

Actually, the explaining wouldn't be to hard. It had all started a couple of days earlier when we in the Brooks office learned that the assistant conservation officer was getting a brand new car. A brand new "K" car to be exact. That prompted Fred, one of the Ducks Unlimited boys, to request my assistance. Fred said he was making some sort of wildlife film. He was nearly finished, had all the shots he needed, except for some good footage of pronghorn antelope — running that is. Fred needed some footage of one of the fastest land animals racing across the prairie.

"I need 'em going flat out," he said. "Stretched right out."

"And you want me to drive?" I asked. This was absurd and illegal but, I had to admit, at the same time, it sounded pretty exciting. I could feel my heart. The beating was getting just a wee bit stronger and louder in the old rib cage.

"Yeah," Fred replied. "I want you to drive. And I want an antelope running right off the front fender."

"Running off the front fender," I repeated. "You want me to break the law and drive you across the prairie at 60 miles an hour. And you want an antelope running off the front fender."

"That's close, but not quite right. You'll probably be doing close to 75 miles an hour, and I want antelope close enough so's I can see the fear in their eyes." Fred chuckled, ignoring the part about the lawbreaking.

"Fear in their eyes, huh. What about the fear in my eyes? You ever seen the size of some of them rocks out on that nice flat prairie. Rocks that seem to jump out of nowhere and ambush unsuspecting oil pans?" I suddenly had a vision of the old green station wagon sitting cold and alone out on the prairie. For a couple of hundred yards behind the old girl, from a point marked by a lone gray rock, there was a black streak and assorted gears, nuts and bolts strewn across the prairie wool. Only the good lord knew just how many rocks I had already hit with the oil pan. And that was driving nice and slow where I could see every little thing that protruded from the earth. At least I thought I could, until the unmistakable sound of metal hitting rock resounded like a clap of thunder. No, the more I thought about the disaster potential, the slower my heart beat. This kind of stunt wasn't for me.

"Don't look at me," I told Fred. "I can hit enough rocks out there when I'm driving slow. In fact, I seem to be able to find them where there aren't any. You go get yourself another maniac."

"You got a free day sometime this week," Fred asked. He seemed to be totally ignoring my refusal.

"Nope," I replied. "Sorry, Fred. I'm booked solid until you finish filming. I don't want nothing to do with it."

Two days later, I received the good word from the Powers-that-be. Fred had been given the necessary approvals to chase the antelope and was to be provided with whatever assistance was necessary to complete his film. Since the old station wagon was to be written off, a statement that I agreed with, for it should have been written off before it was assigned to me, permission was also granted for it to be used for filming purposes.

"It looks like you're it, boy," the boss man informed me when we received the directive.

"Why me?" I asked. "I don't know nothin' about this movie making stuff, anyway."

"For one thing, because the car is your responsibility, it's been assigned to you, and you were told to. And another thing, because I said so. That's why," he smiled.

Now, I don't mind admitting that every time I thought of giving an antelope a run for his money, my heart did a little flip-flop and a few thousand butterflies fluttered around in my stomach. But, there were a lot of unknowns, too, dangers, not the least of which were the ever-present rocks.

"Man, travelling at that speed both you know and I know that I'm gonna hit a rock with that bloody oil pan. I can't even miss them when I crawl across the prairie. What happens if there's any damage to the car?" I asked. "Who pays for that?"

"Don't worry about that. That's a minor detail.

Anyway, that old crate's already been written off. It's just a matter of time till you get a new one. It wouldn't surprise me if it was here before you get back."

"Well, it would certainly surprise me," I replied. "And what happens if I don't get the new one?"

"Well, I guess …. I guess you'll have a problem then, won't you? Yeah, I suppose you'll just have to make do until the new one comes in."

We, Fred and I, had travelled southeast of Brooks into the Ronalane area in our quest for the elusive pronghorn antelope. Preferably, a big elusive buck antelope, a big elusive fast-running buck antelope.

"You must be a one powerful man," I jokingly kidded Fred as I eased old station wagon off the gravel road. Every bolt in the old girl creaked and squeaked as she inched through the ditch and out onto the flat prairie. It was a fine sunny morning. Somewhere out on that flat, grassy surface, beyond my sight, an unsuspecting antelope was relaxing, basking in the sun, completely unaware of the fate that awaited him.

"Well, I am," Fred replied, as if it were a matter of fact and everyone knew it and, if they didn't, well, they should have. "But tell me what makes you think so?"

"Just an observation," I replied as I scanned the horizon searching for an antelope. "Just an observation. Where to, sir?" I asked as the road and all signs of civilization disappeared from sight. Lost, too, were the concerns about the rocks. The concern for the old station wagon. My whole body just tingled with anticipation. Bring on the antelope.

A slight breeze picked up the little dust that rose

from the tires. The dust drifted slowly across the prairie. It might just as well have blown into the old green station wagon I thought, taking a quick glance around the interior. There was dust everywhere. A thin layer lay on the dash, on the seats and, at the end of each day, on me. Dust was a constant reminder of one of the perils of driving across the prairie in the summertime. It was impossible to drive without the windows open because of the intense heat. Driving slow or fast, there was always a cloud of dust behind the vehicle. Stopping or turning down wind resulted in the dust billowing into the car through the open window. The dust was always there.

"I thought that we could just strike out across some of these large leases to the southeast," Fred replied. "How does that sound to you?"

"Sounds fine to me," I replied. "I've never been down here, anyway, so you call the shots. This is your baby. Anyway, I haven't a clue what I'm doing or where I'm going. You just point me in the right direction. I was just told to drive."

"Oh, hell, Bob, relax," Fred grinned. "We're just gonna take a few pictures of some antelope and have some fun."

"How come nobody else wanted to do it then?"

"That's one of the joys of being the new guy on the block," Fred chuckled as we headed south. The ever-present cloud of dust billowed up behind the green station wagon and drifted slowly in the light morning breeze marking our progress.

"There's a bunch," Fred whispered excitedly, and

pointed to a half a dozen animals standing on the skyline off in the distance. They had to be miles away, but I whispered back.

"Right. I got 'em. What now?"

"Keep driving," he directed. "I don't want to spook 'em though, so don't go straight at them. Let's just circle and see how close we can get to them."

I figured the animals were far enough away that a circle would take me to Medicine Hat on the east and Lethbridge on the south. But I circled them. My circle probably wasn't as good as it should have been and the prairie wasn't nearly as flat as it appeared. The antelope on the ridge kept disappearing behind one little knoll after the other. Suddenly, from out of nowhere, we surprised a small herd that had bedded down. When we popped over a little knoll, the startled antelope popped out of their beds like they had been spring loaded. There was about 200 yards distance between the animals and ourselves.

Those little antelope had to be doing 70 miles an hour when their little hooves hit the ground. They shot out ahead of the station wagon like little greased streaks of brown.

"Don't lose 'em," yelled Fred, and the race was on.

I tramped the gas peddle to the floor and the old station wagon answered the call.

"Hurry up. You're losing 'em," Fred yelled, and his voice seemed to be far off, from a distance. I took my eyes off the prairie and the antelope for a second and looked at Fred. I don't know when or how he did it, but he was half out the window. Fred, his head, shoulders, arms, chest and his camera were hanging out the passenger window.

"Stay with 'em," he called again.

"Don't worry," I shouted back. "I've got 'em. You just shoot and I'll drive." I was heading straight for the herd, but not gaining any ground. In fact, I was losing ground rapidly. "How close do you want me to get?" I shouted at Fred's butt. That was the only part of him that seemed to be in the vehicle with me.

"A lot closer then this," he yelled back. "We're too far back."

I had the gas pedal down as far as it would go and slowly the old girl was picking up speed, but now we were just getting a glimpse of the rumps of antelope as they disappeared over the knoll ahead of us. I pushed harder.

Suddenly, I became aware of just how bumpy the prairie terrain actually was. The old station wagon was bouncing and banging around pretty good, as the antelope bounded off across the prairie. I glanced at the speedometer. It was dancing between 45 and 50 miles per hour. The antelope had little difficulty in leaving us behind. Then, they disappeared over one rise in the distance and were gone. When we got to the rise, there was only bald-headed prairie no sign of any living creature. I slowed the car to a crawl and looked at Fred for further direction.

"You're gonna hafta do a lot better'n that," he complained. "I didn't get one shot that was worth a damn."

"Did you see how fast those things can run?" I

asked, just in case Fred hadn't noticed. "I was doing close to 50 and they left us like we were standing still."

"I know," he grumbled. "That's why I haven't got the antelope pictures I need yet."

"Well, where to now?" I asked.

"We keep looking until we find antelope and keep trying until you learn how to drive this thing. That's where," he replied and waved a hand out across the great expanse of prairie that lay before us.

We spotted several small herds of antelope that were not willing to allow us to get close enough to make a run at them. Many would just disappear into the prairie grass long before we arrived on the scene. Others raced off across the prairie at the first sight of the vehicle.

Late in the afternoon, when normal people were home enjoying a nice supper and evening with their families, Fred and I found a small herd of antelope: eight or nine animals that stood on the prairie and curiously watched our approach. They allowed us to get within 100 yards before showing any sign of discomfort.

As the first animal turned and started to walk, Fred yelled: "Step on it!"

I slammed my foot down on the accelerator and, once more, the race was on.

"Faster," Fred screamed. It was his favourite saying when half of him was hanging out the window. "Faster. They're getting away."

I had the pedal to the metal and the old station wagon was slowly gaining speed as I chased the white rumps of the antelope across the prairie. I glanced down at the speedometer, which by now was ranging upwards of 60 miles an hour. I looked at the white rumps again. They weren't getting any closer.

"C'mon, step on it. Faster, man, faster," I heard Fred bellow over the roar of the motor and crashing and banging of the car on the uneven prairie.

"I've got my foot through the floorboard now," I snarled back at him. "This baby is giving it all she's got." But, slowly, the speedometer was creeping up and I could feel the rush of adrenalin. It felt like we were literally flying across the prairie, albeit at a very low altitude. Slowly, we gained on the herd.

"That's it. That's it," yelled Fred excitedly. "That's it. Hold it right there. This is what I've been looking for."

At that point I had a half a dozen antelope running, racing all out, off the right front fender of the green station wagon. They kept getting closer and closer to the vehicle. Then, I realized, they were going to try and cross in front of us. Antelope are crazy that way. I don't know why, but for some strange reason, antelope always want to cross in front of a vehicle. I kept drifting to the left to keep them from hitting the station wagon. Meanwhile, Fred, hanging out the passenger's window, was screaming like a kid with a new toy. I couldn't understand a word he was saying, for I was driving, hell bent for leather, trying to keep the antelope close, just off the right front fender.

Over a small knoll raced the antelope. Over the small knoll sped the car, right at a small cluster of rocks. I swerved to the right. The antelope served to the left. By the grace of God we both missed the rocks, but now the antelope were running off the left front fender and away from us.

"Wrong side," yelled Fred. "They're running on the wrong side of the car."

Fred wasn't telling me anything I didn't know, as the car careened crazily one way then the other as I fought to keep from losing control.

"Get back to the other side," Fred screamed at me, oblivious to what was happening.

The antelope were now running just off the left front fender, trying to cross back in front of the vehicle. Finally, and through absolutely no fault of my own, I got the car under control. I slowed down slightly and the antelope moved across in front of us. Once more Fred had them running off the right front fender.

"That's more like it," he shouted happily when the car had returned to the proper place.

The race was telling, though, and the antelope started to drop by the way. One at a time, an animal would peel away from the herd until there was only one buck left. He maintained his position at the right front of the vehicle and, with his tongue hanging out a yard, he raced on.

We burst over another little rise and instantly we were onto a fire guard: a strip of land that had been opened the width of the blade of a bulldozer. It stretched in both directions across the prairie, across our path. The ridges on both sides were piled about a foot high, studded with rocks of various sizes. The antelope handled the fireguard very well, the station wagon not nearly so. I did not even have time to take my foot off the gas, let alone apply the brakes, before the car hit the first ridge. Rocks and dirt sprayed up and out in front of the car. A rock the size of a softball exploded up in front of the windshield. I thought for a second it was coming through, but it bounced off the top of the car. The station wagon was suddenly airborne. We flew right over the second ridge and the station wagon slammed onto the prairie on the other side of the fire guard. I slammed on the brakes; the race was over. I think Fred would have gone through the windshield had he not been so firmly wedged into the window.

"Take it easy," yelled Fred, who was still hanging out the window. He was now filming the buck that had been running off the front right fender. The buck, too, had called it a race and Fred continued to film the animal , just standing not far off the right fender, looking at the two idiots in the car.

Although the station wagon was stopped, it continued to move. Up and down, up and down it rolled and swayed. A large cloud of prairie dust swirled up and around us, engulfing the rocking vehicle. There were no shocks left, only springs. Sitting in the car was like floating on a cloud. A cloud of dust.

"I think you need a new car," Fred commented as he pulled himself back through the window and settled into the passenger seat, sending the car into another uncontrolled bounce and roll. Fred and I were sweating like a couple of stuck pigs. I don't know about Fred, but I was completely pooped.

I was still pooped when I parked the old station

wagon in front of the office. It was like the passing of an old friend when the rocking and the rolling and the bouncing and the weaving slowly came to a halt. I left the curious townsfolk to pay their final respects and be privy to the final viewing of the old green station wagon that had just spent its last day on the prairie. I went upstairs to prepare for the wake, which would begin with the arrival of a brand new station wagon, and hopefully a pair of new binoculars, possibly a rifle and with a little luck, maybe even a uniform.

ROBERT J. (BOB) ADAMS

Bob Adams was born in Turner Valley, Alberta in 1938. He grew up in the Edson area, in a log house, built by his father on a farm rich in swamp spruce, tamarack, willows and muskeg.

Bob, an avid outdoorsman, was one of the fortunate few who was able to live his boyhood dreams as he entered the workforce. In 1960, after a number of years with the Alberta Forest Service and Royal Canadian Mounted Police, he began a career with the Provincial Government as a Fish and Wildlife Officer. For the next 33 years, he found his homes to include Brooks, Strathmore, Hinton, Calgary, Peace River and Edmonton.

In 1993, after a full career in Enforcement, he retired from Fish and Wildlife and wrote his first book, The Stump Farm. Today, Bob resides in Edmonton, Alberta with his wife Martha where he continues to work on his writing.

GIVE A "ROBERT J. ADAMS" BOOK TO A FRIEND

Megamy Publishing Ltd.
Box 3507
Spruce Grove, AB   T7X 3A7

Send to:

Name:_____

Street:_____

City:_____

Province/   Postal/
State:_____ Zip Code:_____

Please send:

"The Stump Farm"	@ $16.95 =	_____
"Beyond the Stump Farm"	@ $16.95 =	_____
"Horse Cop"	@ $16.95 =	_____
"Fish Cop"	@ $16.95 =	_____
"The Elephant's Trunk"	@ $15.95 =	_____
"The South Road"	@ $16.95 =	_____
Shipping and handling per book	@ $ 4.00 =	_____
7% GST	=	_____
Total amount enclosed:		_____

Make cheque or money order payable to:
Megamy Publishing Ltd.
Price subject to change without prior notice.
ORDERS OUTSIDE OF CANADA must be paid in U.S. funds by
cheque or money order drawn on U.S. or Canadian Bank.
Sorry no C.O.D.'s.

Gift from:
Name:_____
Address:_____
City:_____
Province/   Postal/
State:_____Zip Code:_____

Megamy Publishing will gladly enclose your personal
message with each book sent as a gift.